FROM HERE TO MATERNITY

FROM HERE TO MATERNITY

The Ultimate Survival Guide for New Parents

JOAN McFADDEN

MAINSTREAM
PUBLISHING

EDINBURGH AND LONDON

First published in Great Britain in 1997 by
MAINSTREAM PUBLISHING COMPANY (EDINBURGH) LTD
7 Albany Street
Edinburgh EH1 3UG

ISBN 1 85158 941 4

A catalogue record for this book is available from the British Library

Typeset in Garamond
Printed in Finland by WSOY

With love and thanks to
Jessie Fraser Maclean,
the world's best mum

Contents

Chapter One

Conception and Pregnancy

New challenges are normally made easier by training or by experience gained in similar areas. For example, school smoothes the way into further education, holiday jobs give an indication of what work will be like, and being a member of clubs and societies as a youngster can make adult socialising easier and more fun. Considering becoming a parent is the exception. It doesn't matter if your career has always involved children, if you have spent most of your formative years acquiring a huge fortune as a baby-sitter, or if you are the favourite relative of a host of small children. The changes are so fundamental and the emotions involved so intense – not to mention terrifying – that the most you can hope for is to have all the practicalities covered, so that nothing comes as a surprise.

Some people have always known that they would like a family of their own one day, so the first step for them is relatively straightforward. The rest of us fall roughly into two categories: those who find themselves feeling unusual stirrings of broodiness, and those who inadvertently find parenthood thrust upon them. Both situations present their own agonies. Life as a couple can be very uncomplicated. There may be problems at work or financial worries for either or both of the partners, but these are nothing compared to the concerns which accompany being directly and totally responsible for another person's well-being. In the past, the only time babies have come into the conversation has been in relation to contraception, buying presents for friends who have taken the unusual step of actually giving birth, or as an idea to be contemplated in the distant future.

Then the future catches up with one of you. Initially you pretend it isn't happening, for a number of reasons. If you're a man, it is hardly the most macho thing to admit that the prospect of having a baby of your own is beginning to appeal more than having a season ticket at your favourite football club. For a modern career woman, the stigma lies in the traditional view of women as homemakers, rather than as movers and earthshakers. You ignore the urges and get on with your busy lives, convinced that your partner couldn't be less interested. Eventually, one brave soul broaches the subject in the most casual fashion, and that is it. It might be ignored for weeks but eventually you will start drifting back to it, and at last you move on to The Talk.

Some couples think about having a baby for about three seconds, come up with an unequivocal 'Yes!' and set about procreation with tremendous fervour. Others ponder long and hard, list all the pros and cons and dither endlessly. There are no easy answers. Babies cost a lot in terms of time, money and, sadly, in these enlightened times, career prospects – an area where the woman usually suffers more. No one ever plans for the unexpected. Most couples look at the long-term implications of having a family from the entirely unrealistic viewpoint of the childless, and forget one vital and unpredictable thing in the midst of their careful planning: hormones. Despite rumours to the contrary, this does not apply to women alone. Grown men have been known to turn into gibbering, emotional heaps when confronted by the sight of their own offspring, and in some cases start making sweeping statements of the 'babies should be looked after by their own mothers' type. This is fine if family finances are satisfyingly in the black and likely to stay that way without any contribution from the mother in question, and if she is happy to put her career on hold and turn into Mum for a while.

It is rarely that simple. A lifestyle firmly based on two incomes can be impossible to sustain with limited cash, and following the birth of their child the most laid-back of people can become increasingly worried about rising debt and vastly straitened circumstances. This kind of pressure is the last thing new parents need – which is why it is worth examining all the possibilities at the outset. Compromise should be looked into, and the careful consideration of all options – such as job sharing, shared child-minders or even working from home – can make a final decision easier.

At the risk of sounding sexist, I should point out that this is also the time to consider the most boring of practical implications in having a family. If, as a woman, you're very aware of the biological clock ticking away and have 'persuaded' a not-quite-so-keen partner to try for a baby, then remember all the wild promises you have made to secure his agreement. There is no point in swearing blind that the only change to his life will be some extra strain on his wallet, if deep down you expect him to turn into the ultimate New Man the minute the baby arrives. Be honest. If a reluctant partner agrees to undertake parenthood with a list of criteria, assume that he will stick to them. There is a chance that, like many before him, all he needs to turn him into a perfect husband and father is the arrival of his first-born, but don't be foolish enough to assume that this is a certainty. If you want a baby enough to make a deal about matters such as time, money and chores, then be woman enough to accept that you agreed to these conditions before embarking on the great adventure.

Since the beginning of time, motherhood has often been confused with martyrdom, which can make the decision to go ahead even more harrowing. It is assumed that the very contemplation of parenthood is sufficient to turn the most logical woman into a selfless soul. Nonsense. If you feel too guilt-ridden to admit that your main concern is the loss of your hard-won size 10 figure and a vicious curtailing of your precious free time, rest assured that you are not alone. Most of us feel the same, but secretly suspect that such concerns simply brand us as too frivolous to be excellent mothers. Worrying about your 'unnatural' worries is in fact par for the course, but you do get over it in time, and start 'practising' in earnest.

PRE-CONCEPTION CARE

The theory may be fun, but the practice is even better. However, before caution and contraception are thrown to the wind and you set about making babies with tremendous enthusiasm, it is a good time to think about pre-conception care. There are a number of organisations who make a great deal of money out of pre-conception care, but they should be viewed with caution. You are at a very vulnerable stage when contemplating babies, and therefore represent an easy target to be offered all sorts of advice and tests, all of which seem to guarantee both a perfect pregnancy and a perfect baby. Nobody can guarantee you that, however, and unsurprisingly these blood tests, hair analyses and diet assessments do not come cheap. Hang on to your money and use it for buying a pram a bit later on, and in the meantime make an appointment with your GP or practice nurse.

Pre-conception care is an excellent idea, and while a lot of it is common sense, your doctor or nurse will fill you in with everything else you can do to help both yourself and the prospective baby. It helps if both potential parents are the right sort of weight and fairly fit, if only because this ensures better stamina for the coming months. Extra vitamins should not be necessary at this stage provided you follow a reasonably healthy diet, with one very important exception. It is now recommended that from the time of trying to conceive until 12 weeks pregnant, every woman needs to take 0.4 milligrams of folic acid daily in tablet form, along with their usual dietary intake. Conclusive research has shown that this helps reduce the risk of neural tube defects, such as spina bifida. If there is any family history of spina bifida, or you are taking medication for epilepsy, speak to your doctor before taking folic acid, as further medical advice will be needed. Rubella (German measles) can cause serious damage to the unborn child in the first three months of pregnancy; a simple test by your doctor can establish whether or not you are immune to the disease. If not, it is worth hanging on to the contraception for another few months whilst you are immunised.

There is no evidence that occasional or light drinking in pregnancy will harm your baby, but many women prefer to give up alcohol entirely for the duration of their pregnancy. There is also no research which reveals how many head for the gin bottle immediately after giving birth, or in subsequent weeks of exhaustion! On a more serious note, it is obvious that heavy drinking harms both mother and child, and if you have a problem cutting back, then please look for help before attempting to conceive.

Smoking is often the really tricky one, with loads of intelligent women trying to persuade themselves that 'the odd one' won't do any harm. There is no room for compromise here: if you can't give up smoking, don't get pregnant. If necessary, stop by convincing yourself that once your baby has been born you will smoke yourself stupid. Believe me, the minute you see that little face you will want to live for ever – even if it means giving up something as delightful as nicotine. And I know that it is not easy, but thousands of us manage it.

If you accept that pregnancy means no smoking, then you

won't try any of the little ploys to convince yourself that you're not doing any real harm. One woman I know used to say coyly that her two cigarettes a day was 'just my little treat', ignoring the fact that her indulgence left her son fighting for oxygen in the womb on a regular basis. If you want to, you can kid yourself about anything. When I was in hospital having my first daughter, there was a woman in the next room who had been on bed rest for months due to a condition which was life-threatening for both her and her baby. She told me in all seriousness: 'I'm a very sensitive person; I'm so worried about my baby that I'm smoking 40 a day.' Yes indeed – about as sensitive as an HGV.

It may seem a bit brusque, but smoking endangers your unborn child, does long-term damage to both physical health and intelligence, and is a major factor in cot death. If you want to smoke after the birth and risk leaving your child motherless and possibly suffering from respiratory conditions, then have a go at squaring that with your conscience, but at least have the decency to let the baby have its first nine months as free from poisons as possible.

The same advice applies to recreational or illegal drugs. While the dangers of heroin or crack are well documented, no one knows the long-term effects of cannabis, ecstasy or any other so-called soft drugs on the unborn child and it is therefore best to leave well alone. If you can't, you have no business contemplating pregnancy.

Standard over-the-counter medications should be checked with your doctor or pharmacist, and if you are on medication for conditions such as diabetes or epilepsy then make an appointment with your doctor before becoming pregnant. Sometimes medication needs to be changed, or the dosage may need to be altered throughout the first three months of pregnancy. Similarly, there are some conditions which in the past would have precluded pregnancy, such as heart conditions, physical disabilities or organ transplants. Members of the medical profession rarely generalise about such conditions, and prefer to consider each case individually. Go to your consultant, explain your concerns and ask for advice. If necessary, ask for a second opinion. I interviewed one woman with a serious heart problem who had been summarily dismissed by her consultant with the attitude that she was lucky to have her life; what on earth made her think she could have children? The second specialist she went to spent six months researching her condition and looking at similar cases. There was still some risk during her pregnancies, but by constantly adapting and adjusting her medication and providing superb care, her consultant helped to ensure that she and her husband ended up with two beautiful little boys.

Food rules are fairly straightforward. Take particular care in the preparation of raw meat, washing all surfaces and utensils after use and ensuring that meat and poultry are thoroughly cooked. To prevent the risk of salmonella poisoning, make sure that eggs are also thoroughly cooked, and avoid all types of pâté and ripened soft cheeses because of the risk of listeria infection. Drink only pasteurised or UHT milk, don't eat liver or liver products, and wash all fruit, vegetables and salads carefully. Make sure general hygiene remains good, and always wear gloves or scrub hands thoroughly after handling soil or cat litter. When it comes to exercise, use your common sense and stick to your current methods of staying fit. Now is not the ideal time to take up abseiling or deep-sea diving.

STAYING CALM

Maybe you have spent years studiously avoiding pregnancy, and now you are actively courting it. Despite knowing that it is very unlikely to happen straightaway, you can't help assuming that you will be in the 30 per cent of couples who can conceive within the first month of trying. So there you are, at the peak of physical health, just waiting for it all to happen. And waiting. And waiting. Forget the statistics, or any reassurance from family, friends or even trained medical personnel. You want to be pregnant, and you want to be pregnant now. The first month goes by, and your period arrives as normal. The only way to describe your state of mind is crushed. Logically, you know this could take months, but the minute you decide to procreate, logic goes right out the window. Two months, three, maybe more, and you start to wonder about fertility treatment, whether loose boxer shorts and the crushed ice theory is worth considering, or doing handstands after intercourse. If any of these things make you feel better, go right ahead. They work along the lines of pre-conception care – you feel you are actively contributing something worth while, so you feel a million times better about the whole affair. If you like the idea of controlling your procreation, there is a fair chance that you might also fancy the idea of choosing your baby's sex. There are lots of theories on this, usually involving diet – but no proof that any of them work. At any given time there is a 50:50 chance that one of them will appear to be successful, so if it makes you feel good, then do it! Good luck, and I hope you get what you want.

The majority of couples will manage to conceive by themselves, but it can be difficult not to panic. Some people will undoubtedly need further advice or medical intervention, but professionals suggest giving it a year of trying before heading back to your doctor. They will then look at your medical history and you can consider all the options together. For the rest, a few words of advice during the first months of trying – don't be, if you can possibly avoid it. Try not to worry each other silly by going on and on incessantly about your current lack of success in conceiving, and don't start boring family or friends either. People are initially very understanding, but patience can wear thin very quickly.

Now is the time to sublimate all your maternal/paternal longings either by buying a good guidebook to pregnancy and parenthood or by starting to subscribe to one of the many magazines which focus entirely on the subject. This approach will either bore you so much that you automatically become less obsessed, or – more likely – will pander to your insatiable appetite for endless information on the joys of parenthood. However, I do suggest that you keep to your usual reading matter in public, and either read these publications in the bath or pore over them in bed. Which leads me to the next point: try not to pore over anything much in bed other than each other. Do not turn your sex life into some kind of procreation rite and always remember what got you interested in each other to begin with. It certainly wasn't an initial summing-up of your partner's potential as a parent. In addition, assuming that sooner rather than later you will be successful in your quest, you can rest assured that there is a fair chance that for some time to come your sex life will undergo some radical changes! Surprisingly, many of these will be good.

Good sense eventually prevails: you calm down and life resumes a more normal routine. However, at the back of your mind you are always aware of the possibility of becoming pregnant, and you modify your lifestyle accordingly. And one day it just happens. Some women say that they know from the moment of conception, which I always heartily mocked until I became pregnant for the first time. A week before my period was due I just felt different, although I couldn't pinpoint the exact cause. I had none of the early pregnancy symptoms listed in my countless guidebooks, just a strange sensation that something new was happening in my body. We tried a home testing kit but it was really too early, and the indicator went a sort of creamy pink rather than the shocking vermilion I had been waiting for. Undaunted, I gave it another week and the second testing kit was a resounding POSITIVE. Incidentally, this experience never repeated itself as in my two subsequent pregnancies I was well into my sixth week before I became aware of any changes.

However you find out, and however much you have longed for it, a positive result leaves you reeling. You may be jumping up and down for joy, you may be thinking 'what have we done?', you may even be going through both sensations at once. And I am assuming that this confused reaction is coming from a couple who have hoped for just this event – imagine having it sprung on you unexpectedly! Suddenly discovering that an unplanned baby is on the way can be enough of a shock for two people in a secure and committed relationship, but contemplating life as a single parent with little money could reduce the calmest person to hysterics. Each situation is unique, and everyone involved in it has to look for the best solution for both parents and child. Fortunately there is no longer the stigma attached to illegitimacy which determined so many marriages in the past, and no one should allow themselves to be forced into anything simply to bow to convention or placate upset grandparents.

Single Parenthood

If things are getting a bit fraught, it can be beneficial to bring in an impartial outsider, such as a counsellor, to help the two of you consider the future. It is tempting and very understandable to take cover in tempestuous scenes of emotion and blame, but there comes a point where practical considerations must take priority. Life will obviously be a bit easier if you intend to continue with some kind of interactive relationship, but in many cases that is no longer feasible. Should this be the case, parental responsibility cannot be shrugged off any more than it can be in any other relationship, and the parents have to share the financial implications of having a child. If money is a concern, along with fears of being unemployed, contact the DSS Freeline, local social security office or the Citizens Advice Bureau. The local housing office will be able to give advice on housing concerns.

It can also help to speak to others who have gone through pregnancy on their own, and the self-help organisation Gingerbread is an ideal starting-point, with a network of local groups. The National Council for One-Parent Families can also supply information on a wide range of relevant subjects, from benefits to maintenance. It is also worth finding out who your health visitor is, although – at the risk of making a sweeping generalisation – I should mention that all the mums I have contact with describe their health visitors as either 'brilliant' or 'useless'. There seems to be no middle ground here; it appears to be purely a matter of luck, and keeping your fingers crossed that yours will fall into the first category.

If you don't have a partner you are under enough pressure, so please don't feel that you have to cope with antenatal visits and labour by yourself. A friend, a sister or your mum will be made welcome at the hospital, and you will be treated as well as everybody else, if not better. Nurses and midwives like to promote a cool, professional image but it seems that they also have a natural talent for taking the most vulnerable firmly under their wings. The petrified 15-year-old schoolgirl in one of my antenatal classes was not only accompanied and cared for by her own mother and grandmother, but gently encouraged and reassured by every midwife in the place. Ask for help. Sometimes you simply cannot cope alone, but people may wait for you to make the first move, worried about interfering or appearing patronising.

SUCCESS

So you've managed to convince yourself that the test was correct, and you trot off to the doctor, who calmly confirms your initial diagnosis. This is the moment when you start to suspect that the entire world does not revolve around your pregnancy, as he/she shows no signs of dancing around the surgery in joy and wonder. You are slotted into the antenatal system, and the different types of care are explained (these may vary slightly throughout the country). In general, though, there are usually three main options. If you are planning to have your baby in hospital there are two types of care within this system. You will either visit the hospital for every check-up or, more usually, have what is referred to as 'shared care', with check-ups divided equally between the hospital and your own doctor. If you plan to have your baby in a GP/midwife unit, or at home, then you will probably see your own doctor or community midwife for most of your antenatal care. However, when you consider that your booking visit is normally at around thirteen weeks and your initial visit to the doctor takes place at around six or seven weeks, that leaves about six weeks to get through before you start to feel part of a recognisable system.

The chances are that you will deal with this situation completely differently from your partner. Men sometimes feel that the initial euphoria has worn off and that they are now in a strange hiatus, with no outward physical signs to give even a hint of the great event. So they just get on with life – which can drive a hormonally challenged, first-time-pregnant woman simply demented. Here they are, going through the biggest change in their life to date, and the man concerned does not want to spend every available second discussing any and every fascinating aspect of pregnancy. Calm down. In a few months' time, when you have reached that peculiar madonna-like calm which claims all women eventually, you will have your revenge. He will be running around like the proverbial headless chicken – especially when you go into labour – while you watch him go through all the emotions you came to terms with early on in your pregnancy.

If a sister or close friend is pregnant around the same time, this provides the best therapy of all, but sadly not everyone is willing to synchronise their husbands just to keep you happy. However, if this happens by chance, then make the most of it, as you can bore each other rigid with your delightful obsession and retain some semblance of calm and normality for the rest of the world. If you want to wander around Mothercare and sigh a lot, don't be put off. Hugging your secret and stroking tiny baby clothes is your privilege. If you have the sort of mum who will be ecstatic at your news but can keep a secret, then tell her, and experience an entirely new relationship with the woman who went through it all for you. This is a lovely time for both of you, and in many ways it is like joining the grown-ups while still having the pleasure of being someone else's little girl. Mums are particularly good when it comes to admitting all the niggling little concerns you don't want to tell your doctor, and it is very reassuring to be told: 'Oh, I had that with all five of you!'

EARLY SYMPTOMS

There must be some women out there who take all this in their stride, but I don't know anyone who remained unruffled during their first pregnancy. Since the first three months are also the time when you don't tell the world at large, you can end up feeling very isolated, especially if you have any unpleasant symptoms to contend with. Maternity leave at the beginning would be ideal for some, especially those who bloom for the last six months. Two of the most common problems at the beginning are tiredness and nausea. The most peculiar thing about this is that despite the fact they can be so devastating at the time, you forget all about them between pregnancies. This must be some cruel trick of nature to ensure the survival of the human race. The fatigue is like nothing you have ever known, and you can't help but wonder if you haven't

21

contracted some fatal illness as you drag yourself around the place. Never mind going to bed early – staying up for *Coronation Street* starts to constitute wild living! Throw in a touch of morning sickness – or afternoon, evening or all-day sickness, as it can also be known – and you start to wonder what the joy of parenthood is all about. On particularly bad days, as you sit grey-faced at work and fantasise about three weeks in bed – alone – while colleagues suggest you might have everything from flu to malaria, concentrate on two things. Pamper yourself, and remember: things can only get better.

Now is the time when the handy reference book comes into its own. There are many to choose from, but I shall stick my neck out and categorically state that the best ever has to be *Pregnancy* by Gordon Bourne. Written over 20 years ago but updated regularly, this is the one book which covers everything you could think of and more. The author is quite authoritarian and includes absolutely nothing wishy-washy or sentimental in 600 pages, but he tells it like it is. Read it while you are lying pathetically on your bed, and feel a whole lot better for knowing that thousands of other women have felt this bad, survived and gone and done it again. Tell your partner that you feel awful, if he hasn't already guessed, and do as little as possible until you feel better. There are lots of old wives' tales about morning sickness, and some of them do actually work. Ginger biscuits and ginger beer sometimes help, as do very plain biscuits or crackers. Fizzy mineral water was my salvation, along with pressure wristbands normally used to combat travel sickness. It can be tempting to avoid food altogether but try not to do this, as you just end up feeling twice as bad with weakness on top of the sickness. The only solution for the fatigue is rest and sleep, wherever and whenever you can. Don't worry if you feel resentful, let down or fed up, as sainthood does not automatically land on you at the same time as fertilisation. Some other strange side-effects can start making themselves known, such as an obsession for particular smells. If you ever see a woman standing in a petrol station and breathing the petrol vapours as if they were the sweetest perfume, you can bet your bottom dollar that she is pregnant.

The experts will tell you that these symptoms will ease off around weeks 12 to 14. The good news for the majority of women is that this is, in fact, usually the case. The bad news for a few is that they just go on and on and on, sometimes up to 20, 30 or, worst of all, 40 weeks. I am really sorry, but I can't think of one constructive word of comfort in these cases. Nobody should blame you for being a disgruntled, petulant harpy for the entire nine months – but they still will. This is motherhood, and you are expected to bear it patiently and bravely. If it is in your nature to go for the stiff-upper-lip approach then do it, but I would suggest finding a sister or close friend who is an expert at offering a sympathetic shoulder. Also, remember the man who got you into all this, and if it helps to make his life a misery, just go right ahead. He might never agree to a second child, but he will forgive all the whining the minute he claps eyes on this one.

Reaching the third month safely is the first watershed. With any luck you will be Mrs Average, and sickness and tiredness will start to ease off. You will have entire days where you feel almost human, and you might even consider being nice to your partner again. Bear in mind that the three months have probably not been the most pleasant of his life, and it must be rather nice for him to see the woman of his dreams start to re-emerge from the disgruntled, green-faced changeling who has been haunting his home. Then you have your first scan, and nothing in a million years could prepare either of you for the breathtaking excitement of this moment. Suddenly it is all worth while, because there in front of you is a fuzzy, wriggling little thing, who admittedly resembles nothing more than ET. But you can see the heartbeat, and a nurse or doctor will happily and patiently point out all the precious little bits and pieces. Some hospitals give you a photograph, and it is almost like permission to go out and tell the world – which is exactly what you do.

Antenatal care can seem a bit bewildering, but make sure you ask if you don't understand anything. Always take a stock of magazines or a good book with you, as waiting times can be lengthy. The first visit will probably last the longest, as the staff take the opportunity to catalogue your history and make sure they have all the relevant information regarding family illnesses, work and ethnic origin. They will note down the date of your last period to assess the baby's estimated due date, and check weight, blood pressure and general health. Blood tests will also be taken at this visit to check the blood group, whether you are rhesus negative or positive, anaemic or immune to rubella, or whether you suffer from syphilis or hepatitis B. You will be asked to provide a urine sample at every visit, which can give staff an immediate indication of possible problems, such as an infection or high blood pressure.

Antenatal checks should be reassuring and informative, but it can be difficult to remember all your queries when faced by the professionals. Note down questions if necessary, as it can be very hard to bear niggling doubts and worries until the next check-up is due. Most of the staff are superb but you can have personality clashes, and whilst pregnancy is notorious for turning the most mild-mannered woman into Attila the Hun, if you really don't like something or somebody make your feelings known politely and find out if you could see someone else instead. Your partner can come to any of the classes with you, and there is usually a tour of the labour suite later on in the pregnancy for both the prospective mother and her birth partner. If you and your partner don't want him at the birth, and you would rather have Mum, Aunty Lil or your best pal, then the choice is yours. Don't feel under any pressure to do things by the book.

As the weeks and months go by, you discover all the other little joys which make childbearing such a breeze, such as backache, cramp and varicose veins, or the really dignified ones such as constipation, heartburn and piles. Don't suffer in silence. If you have any major concerns such as bleeding, severe cramps or serious headaches, contact your doctor immediately. Alternatively, the midwives at your hospital or health centre are just a phone call away, and have endless patience – along with their endless patients! They have seen it all before and so are reassuringly confident, but they know that it is all new to you and are usually both kind and helpful.

ANTENATAL TESTS

There comes a moment in every pregnancy when you wonder if your baby is all right, and whether it is 'normal'. Reactions to this differ greatly, and if there is a family history of a particular condition you will probably have been aware of all the implications when you considered conception. There are different tests available to determine various conditions, and you can make an appointment to discuss this with the pre-conception care team at your hospital at any time before conceiving or as soon as you know you are pregnant. You do not have to wait until you are in the middle of your antenatal care, although some tests have to be done later rather than early on. Maternal age is a factor in whether or not you are offered some of these tests, on the assumption that certain risks increase when the woman is over a particular age. However, there are a number of points to bear in mind before opting for further tests. Every maternity hospital has a cut-off age (often 35, 37 or 39), and if you are this age or above you will be offered an appointment to discuss any risks. This is simply an offer and is by no means mandatory; if you do not wish to take up the appointment then feel free to say so. If you do take up the appointment the staff are there only to help and inform, and no pressure is ever put on you to take any tests.

Alpha-fetoprotein (AFP) is a widely available test performed between 15 and 20 weeks which can indicate a risk of spina bifida or Down's syndrome. This is non-invasive and can give only an indication of risk, rather than a definitive answer. However, if your level of risk is higher than average you may be offered a detailed ultrasound scan. Again, this is non-invasive and the operator is looking for 'soft markers' which can be present along with particular conditions.

The two tests which can give the most accurate information are amniocentesis and chorionic villus sampling. Both carry a small miscarriage risk: less than 1 per cent with amnio-centesis, and 2–3 per cent with chorionic villus sampling. In the first case, an ultrasound scan is performed at the same time to check the position of the baby and placenta, and a needle is passed through the abdomen into the amniotic fluid which surrounds the baby. A sample of fluid is withdrawn and sent for analysis, which can give a definitive answer for both spina bifida and Down's. This test will also reveal the baby's sex. CVS is performed in the same way, although this time a small piece of the developing placenta is withdrawn. It cannot show up spina bifida, but will reveal Down's and various other disorders. In both cases it takes one to two weeks to obtain the results. In theory, neither test is meant to be particularly painful. Whilst this appears to be true of amniocentesis, I have spoken to a number of women who have had CVS who found it extremely uncomfortable, with severe cramping afterwards. They did, however, all point out that they were extremely tense during the test, which would certainly have made it more painful than was strictly necessary.

Waiting for the test results is the hardest part, because you are aware that there is a possibility that you will have to make further and harder decisions. You will never be pressured by medical staff into making a particular decision, and whatever you choose to do is entirely up to you. Some couples know that they would never consider termination, and simply wish to be prepared if they will be looking after a baby with special needs. Others may make the decision not to continue with the pregnancy, and in both instances there are local support groups made up of people who have been through the same experience. Remember that the vast majority of pregnancies have a happy outcome, but if you find yourself going through the trauma of having a child with special needs, or opting for a termination, remember that you need time to grieve and come to terms with what has happened (see chapter 9).

As your pregnancy becomes more apparent it is only polite to tell your employer of your plans for the future. Every woman who is in work while pregnant is entitled to paid leave to attend antenatal classes and to 14 weeks' paid maternity leave. The earliest you can start your leave is 11 weeks before the week your baby is due, and you can work right up until the week of childbirth if you are fit to do so. However, if you have a pregnancy-related illness in the last six weeks your employer can insist that you start your maternity leave at this time. For the first six weeks of maternity leave you are entitled to 90 per cent of your average pay, and the remainder of the time to the basic rate of statutory maternity pay, which is currently £54.55 weekly. This is only the statutory allowance and many firms are more generous with both time and allowance, so check your conditions of service or ask your personnel department. You may also qualify for up to 29 weeks' unpaid leave after the initial 14 weeks. Women who have paid national insurance contributions for at least 26 of the 66 weeks before the baby is born should be entitled to maternity allowance if they cannot get statutory maternity pay. This still applies if you are self-employed or if you gave up work or changed jobs during your pregnancy. Contact your local social security office for details and the relevant forms.

The months move on and from being an almost incidental part of your life, your pregnancy starts to take over in a big way. Enjoy it. Ignore all the little niggles as much as possible and flaunt your bump. There is no rule to say you have to dress in boring maternity gear, and there are now lots of different outlets providing a wide (pardon the pun) range of clothes which are both comfortable and trendy. In this instance, big is undoubtedly beautiful. Even parts of your body which have no right to be affected by pregnancy can be, such as your feet – you can find yourself going up an entire shoe size by the time you give birth. Pamper yourself, and start indulging in all the planning, buying and anticipation of the last few months.

Chapter Two

The Birth and Early Days

At around six or seven months the baby really starts making its presence felt, and the kicks, twists and turns lead you to suspect that your child has a great future as a boxer. It is also a time when, with any luck, you will feel in the best of health, and the resulting emotions can leave you very confused. Sometimes you are totally enchanted by the way this tiny person has taken over your body, and yet at other times you feel as if you have got a bit part in *Alien* which you're certainly not enjoying! Forget about the traditional motherhood/pregnancy images which are so prevalent, and accept that there are days when you will feel fat, invaded and resentful. You have never even met this person who is inflicting all these physical and emotional changes on you, but the public at large assume that you automatically love the child and are eagerly awaiting its arrival.

That is fine, if you can also accept that for every couple who are breathless with excitement at the imminent arrival of a child whom, they feel, they already love, there is another couple who are terrified by the entire experience and worry constantly that they won't even like the baby. I spent my first pregnancy convinced that labour would be like being on the wrong side of the Spanish Inquisition, and that when the baby arrived I would change my mind about the whole thing. I then spent my second pregnancy under the impression that labour would be as easy as falling off a log, but that there was no way I would love my second child as much as my first. An hour after she was born I was ready to choose names for my third!

PLAN AHEAD

It is very irritating to be told this by someone who has already done it, but the best thing you can do is try and stay calm. Be very logical with yourself. Tell yourself that if you don't like motherhood then you will plunge back into your career and pay for the best childcare available. In your maddest moments, reassure yourself that if you really, really hate it all, then there are loving couples queuing up to adopt babies. Look nastily at all the people you cannot stand but who seem to be reasonable parents, and think how much better you will be than them. When the baby arrives your reaction will be nothing like you have imagined, but every reaction is 'normal'. Instant love and bonding, weeks of nothing more than familiarity before love takes over, complete confidence, utter terror at the prospect of the responsibility – it happens differently to everyone. Think about it and imagine what it might be like, but don't expect it to turn out the way you have planned. It very rarely does.

The later antenatal classes are fun because you feel that D-Day is actually in sight, but no antenatal class would be complete without the class bore. Despite having no medical training whatsoever, this barrel of laughs knows everything there is to know about childbirth, and thinks nothing of correcting the midwife. We used to arrive early at the class in the hope of not being stuck beside our particular nightmare, but I really drew the short straw when it came to giving birth. While I was asking for every medical intervention known to man, she was in the next room breathing deeply and easing her son into the world after a two-minute labour. As I was recovering from my Caesarean section the following day, her words of comfort were: 'What a shame you didn't manage to do it by yourself and, never mind, better luck for a boy the next time.' I gazed at the most beautiful baby girl imaginable, and found myself speechless for the first time in 30 years!

The hospital will provide you with a list of essentials for your stay, and packing your bag really makes you feel that things are starting to happen. It is worth adding a few extras to make life more comfortable, such as disposable pants and a favourite brand of sanitary towels. The ones provided by the hospital are usually enormous and leave you walking like John Wayne, which doesn't do a lot for your natural grace and elegance. Make-up and perfume (remember to spray it down the back of your neck after you give birth, or you will have the entire ward wondering what your baby's allergic to) help to make you feel more human, as do your own clothes to wear during the day. You're not ill, and it does help to get into a routine of feeling presentable. Don't be over-ambitious and bring your size 8 jeans, but comfy leggings and some bright T-shirts and blouses make you feel a whole lot better. On the most basic note possible, I would also suggest that you stick a J Cloth and a bottle of Dettox in a plastic bag so you can give the bath a quick going over before using it; NHS cuts are most often reflected in areas like hygiene and the pleasure of a hot soak is vastly diminished by the prospect of relaxing in someone else's dirt.

Have a small labour bag ready, with things like tapes, cartons of juice, two good books (one for each of you!) and mints, and if you go into labour in the middle of the night, force your partner to make himself a couple of sandwiches. Most hospitals have catering machines available at all hours, but the darling probably won't want to leave your side, even for a cup of tea. A rumbling tum can be extremely distracting during critical moments. Remember the anxious grannies waiting for news, and include a list of relevant telephone numbers and lots of change or phone cards. Many hospitals do not allow the use of mobile phones because they can interfere with some medical equipment, so make sure you check their policy on this before bringing one in. Don't take large amounts of cash, credit cards or loads of precious jewellery, but make sure you have got enough money to buy a paper or a magazine to occupy the occasional moment when you're not gazing in stunned adoration at your baby.

Understandably, prospective parents tend to be very superstitious about buying baby clothes and equipment, but you will have to do a certain amount of forward planning.

It is quite a shock to realise what an impact a baby has on your bank balance, but I would suggest that you try not to get carried away. Your baby needs somewhere to sleep with appropriate bedding, a bath or basin and a couple of soft towels for his/her exclusive use, and the correct car seat if you use a car. If well-meaning friends or family offer a second-hand crib, cot or pram, then check that they meet the British Safety Standards, buy a new mattress and away you go. If you can afford a new car seat then buy one; it is better than buying a second-hand one with an unknown history and having no knowledge of whether the safety straps have become worn or have been strained in an accident. Some hospitals have a car seat lending scheme to see you through the first few months; check if this applies in your area.

If you can afford to, save up and splash out a bit – buying all the equipment is terrific fun. Work colleagues wanting to give you a leaving present should be gently pointed in the direction of Mothercare or Early Learning Centre vouchers, as both these stores provide everything your heart desires to welcome your baby into the world. There are specialist pram centres which cover everything from four-poster cots to buggies for triplets, but they do have a tendency to follow prevailing fashions. This is understandable if it is what the customers want, but seeing as nursery goods are hardly the cheapest items to change every time something goes out of fashion, my personal preference is for the traditional experts. Furthermore, the staff in places like Mothercare and the Early Learning Centre do not go for the 'hard sell' approach, and prefer to treat customers as individuals. They must get some sort of training which makes them accustomed to dealing with dreamy-looking pregnant women who can spend hours picking just the right bath, or get themselves totally confused over something as basic as a navy pram.

Take a friend who already has at least one child along with you, but leave the child at home as this is a long shopping trip. Talk to the experts about your major purchases. Think practical, as well as pretty. There is no point in buying a huge carriage pram if you live three floors up in a building with no lift. Will you be in and out of the car, or on and off buses, having to fold up a buggy with one hand? Do you want the baby in your bedroom for the first year, and if so, just how big a cot can you wedge into the space beside your bed? A baby sling is an excellent purchase, as it can provide not only easy transport for the first few months, but also a very comfortable (for you) and comforting (for the baby) means of keeping a fractious or colicky child close to you. The usual procedure is that you order your equipment and pay a deposit, and then uplift your purchases when your baby has safely arrived.

Your hospital will also provide a list of clothing your baby will need, suggesting that you keep it fairly basic as babies grow out of clothes long before they wear them out. Some hospitals prefer the baby to be dressed in hospital gowns during your stay, while others are quite happy for you to bring in your own garments. They do not, however, provide a laundry service for your own clothes, so get your partner practising his hand-washing skills!

WAITING TIME

So, you are now as organised as you can be, and it is time to wait and enjoy your maternity leave. First maternity leave is the best, if only because it is so self-indulgent. There is time to go out for lunches, catch up with friends and spend lots of time with your partner. These last few weeks before your baby arrives can be a very romantic time, with plenty of opportunities to relax and enjoy life. Late in pregnancy you reach a curious plateau; it is a waiting time where you are quite calm and contented but very aware that the last few weeks are flying by. Reactions vary dramatically. Some women feel very attractive and leap on their partner at every available opportunity, while others put all their energies into nest-building and keeping the ironing up to date. Each to their own.

Nature has a way of making the prospect of giving birth very appealing. Every woman reacts differently to her pregnancy, some feeling constantly fat, unattractive and ill whilst others feel glowing and feminine. In the last couple of weeks we all come to the same point: a realisation that we have had quite enough of this and it is time to get on with the next part of our lives. It doesn't matter if you have spent nine months planning a water birth with no intervention, or convinced that you will spend the entire labour screaming in agony – at some point you just accept that it is time to go. What will be, will be, after all.

In your hospital bag you will no doubt have your birth plan, which you will have discussed endlessly with your partner and your midwife. It is an excellent reference guide, but remember that it is not carved in stone. If you want to change your mind at any time just tell the staff, and remember that they have the good of your child in mind when they make suggestions.

The worst thing about labour is that the first time you have no idea what it is going to be like, and the second time you know exactly what it is going to be like! However, speaking as someone who was petrified of going into labour, I would like to pass on the most reassuring piece of advice that I was given. Vague remarks like 'it's like bad period pains' or 'you soon forget' only made me feel worse, but I felt a lot better when my mum (midwife and mother of five) calmly said: 'Yes, it can be really sore, but you'll get all the pain relief you want, it doesn't last for ever, and it's worth it for what you get at the end.' That seemed reasonable, and my subsequent 14-hour labour and Caesarean section holds very fond memories for me, cushioned as it was by gas and air, diamorphine and an epidural.

Rumour has it that if you go into labour in Marks and Spencers they give you an entire layette as a gift, but I wouldn't recommend haunting their food hall in the hope that your waters break at the right time. If they do break somewhere public, just look brave and long suffering and people will rush to your aid. On no account look embarrassed. It is very unlikely that the baby will arrive immediately, and a phone call to the hospital will confirm this. The majority of women experience Braxton Hicks' contractions throughout their pregnancies, which could almost be described as the uterus practising for the big event. As you near the end of the nine months they become stronger and more obvious, and can help to prepare you for the real thing.

The experts at the antenatal clinic will give you a fairly comprehensive list of the different ways in which labour can start, ranging from waters breaking, the onset of regular contractions or a 'show', which is a sort of pinkish-brown discharge indicating that the plug of mucus in the cervix has come away. Please remember that the experts have to use generalisations when dealing with something as individual as the onset of labour, and although some women will undoubtedly follow the book, lots more of us go our own sweet way.

It is quite a good idea to put a rubber sheet on your bed in the last few weeks in case your waters break while you're asleep, but it depends if you can bear to be even hotter and have weirder dreams than you are already experiencing. These bizarre and amazingly realistic dreams are characteristic of pregnancy, but at times they can leave you very shaken and wondering if you have developed Cassandra-like tendencies. I decided that my recurring nightmare of giving birth to a Labrador pup was a direct result of the vicious heartburn which plagued the end of my pregnancy, and tried to forget all about it. Disturbed sleep is common, whether it is the result of discomfort or nature simply preparing you for the broken nights ahead, but it can also be a very intimate feeling, especially if your baby is also awake. Feeling a little foot squirming about or stroking what can only be a tiny bottom wriggling from side to side can help to allay the panic about what is to come.

When it does all start to happen, you will be amazed at your reaction. All your worries and doubts are put on hold, while you concentrate on getting through the experience. In my first pregnancy, my waters broke at one o'clock in the morning (and yes, thank goodness for the rubber sheet or the mattress would never have been the same again!) and I made a mad dash for the toilet, where I sat and contemplated my navel, wondering what would happen next. It was a hot summer night and I was perched naked on the loo, gazing into a full-length mirror. When you're less than five feet tall and nine months pregnant you are undoubtedly a lovely sight, and all I could do was giggle hysterically. Then my first contraction hit. Every thought of panic disappeared and I realised that within a day I would be meeting my baby for the first time. It was time to do it and any terror just evaporated as I got on with the job in hand.

This is a common reaction, although I have heard it described as simply being resigned to having no other option. Phone the hospital and take their advice. If you would like to spend the next few hours floating around at home then relax and just do it. However, if you would feel much safer in hospital then tell your midwife and the chances are that you will be admitted. A few poor souls find themselves in false labour and get sent home, which is immensely frustrating, especially as you then start to worry that you won't recognise the real thing.

At the other end of the scale you have labour which refuses to start. Your due date comes and goes, and you get heartily sick of the persistent 'you're still here!' jokes. Self-help measures abound, with varying degrees of comfort. The worst ever has to be a dose of castor oil, with the assumption that an attack of diarrhoea will trigger labour. A very hot curry is also high on the list, working along similar lines, but apparently the only theory with any scientific basis is a satisfying sex session, as semen contains prostaglandins which play an important part in ripening the cervix and inducing contractions. My suggestion is to go for your own preference, although in terms of enjoyment only one of these methods would get my vote! When all else has failed and the baby stays firmly in place well after 40 or 41 weeks most hospitals now advocate induction, which usually follows a set pattern. Prostaglandin pessaries or gels are administered to ripen the cervix, followed by rupture of the membranes. It is quite likely that this will be sufficient to put you straight into labour, but where this is not the case the hormone oxytocin will be administered, normally by intravenous drip.

Irrespective of how you begin, you will find yourself firmly ensconced in a labour room, with infuriatingly calm nursing staff and a fairly petrified partner. What do you do if your partner cannot bear the thought of being present at the birth, and you can't bear the thought of being there without him? This is a really difficult one to resolve and there is no definitive answer which will keep everyone happy. If at all possible, try to get it sorted out before your contractions start. Each person's reservations will be based on genuine fears, which makes the situation even more fraught. You can understand a man feeling squeamish or upset at the thought of his partner in pain, but you can also understand a woman feeling rejected and upset if the father of her child cannot stand there and hold her hand.

At the risk of sounding sexist, I have to say that I think this is one time when the chaps should be selfless and put their partner's wishes first. First of all, it is hard enough to go through a first-time labour at the best of times, let alone facing it on your own. You will be surrounded by the finest medical attention, caring and professional staff, and the best facilities available. When it comes to the crunch, however, none of this means much without the support and encouragement of the person who helped you get into this situation in the first place. Secondly, no matter how worried the men might be about showing themselves up by being squeamish or by passing out, the midwives are always one step ahead of them. The last thing they need is some grey-faced character lying on the floor requiring stitches to a nasty head wound, and so they keep a keen eye out for potential casualties. In my local hospital, the (secret) policy is to announce 'Tea for all the dads!' in a loud voice and usher them all into the waiting-room if it appears that any of them is coming to the end of his tether. This is an excellent face-saving device which lumps all the men firmly together and pre-empts any nasty situations. Having practised their tea-drinking and male-bonding skills, they return refreshed and ready to go.

Meanwhile, you would give your eyeteeth for a cup of tea, but you have to make do with sucking ice instead. I am not going to attempt to generalise about labour, apart from in one area. If you honestly believe that enduring pain stoically and without relief makes you a better person, then on you go, but please don't attempt to enforce these beliefs on anyone else. Pain in labour varies enormously, and there is an appropriate level of pain relief available for every situation. Go back to your birth plan, and adapt it as the situation develops. A change of position, massage, being held by your partner, distraction through music or walking about, and the use of water, both in conventional baths and showers and in birthing pools, can all contribute to your comfort along with the more conventional methods of pain relief.

The TENS method, or transcutaneous electrical nerve stimulation, is a non-invasive form of pain relief. Four electrodes are taped on to your back and connected by wires to a small battery-powered stimulator, which you control to give yourself small, safe amounts of current. Apparently this method works by stimulating the body to produce its own natural painkillers, known as endorphins, and reducing the number of pain signals sent to the brain. As with all other forms of pain relief opinion is divided, although the main criticism I have heard is that it is rather cumbersome if you would like an active labour. Those who have found the TENS method effective are ready to swear by it, so I would suggest that you find out as much as possible about it beforehand.

Entonox is frequently referred to as 'gas and air', and is another method which you will probably be encouraged to practise in antenatal classes. You breathe it in through a mask which you hold for yourself, so it is easy to control. Although it can make you feel a little light-headed, there are no harmful effects on either you or your baby, and if you are one of the few who feel sick or sleepy you can stop using it immediately, with no lasting effects. I found it really effective during my first labour, and it helped my husband and me to develop a very reassuring double act. I was attached to a machine monitoring my contractions, which he learned to follow very quickly so that he could tell me every time another one was looming. (Naturally, we eventually reached a point where I knew long before he did, but that's another story!) Since the gas takes 15 to 20 seconds to work it is best taken at the beginning of a contraction, so with his encouragement I felt very much in control of my pain.

If this does not give you enough relief, or if it starts to wear off after a while, you can ask for an injection, which usually comes in the form of diamorphine. It will last for two to four hours, but can have some side effects such as dizziness, nausea and, in a few unfortunates, actual vomiting. However, on the positive side, it can also induce sleepiness, and forty winks in the middle of labour can make all the difference when it comes to conserving your strength. It can, however, also make your baby very sleepy and affect its breathing, so the medical staff will not administer this method of pain relief if you are close to delivering. There is no need for concern if you have been given the drug and your baby is then born more quickly than expected, as there is an antidote available to counteract any adverse effects.

An epidural anaesthetic is a special type of local anaesthetic which provides total pain relief for most women. It must be given by a trained anaesthetist, and involves the insertion of a very thin tube between the bones of the spine, allowing the anaesthetic to be pumped in continuously or topped up when necessary. The disadvantages of this method are centred on the resultant inability to feel any sensations at all, which means that you are unable to get out of bed and may have to have a catheter inserted and a drip set up to provide necessary fluids.

There is also the possibility of backache or headaches for some time afterwards. On a personal note, I found the epidural an excellent method of pain relief which perked me up beautifully, had no after-effects, and in essence gave me a much-needed second wind. As I then went on to have a Caesarean section, everything was already in place to ensure a smooth delivery.

THE BIRTH AND INITIAL REACTIONS

Labour is always described as being in three stages, beginning with the cervix opening up until it is fully dilated. This is followed by the baby being pushed down the vagina and being born, and finally by the placenta coming away from the wall of the womb and being pushed out. In a first labour, the time from the start of established labour to full dilation can vary from six to twelve hours on average, and is often quicker in subsequent labours. Towards the end of the first stage you may feel you want to push, and this is a time when you will be guided by your midwife, who is obviously viewing things from a slightly different angle. She may tell you to wait until the cervix is fully dilated and the baby's head can be seen, which sounded fine in the antenatal classes but doesn't seem so simple when you're in the middle of it. This is where the famous breathing exercises come into their own, and you can blow out or puff gently to help yourself get over the urge to push.

The second stage can make you feel that the baby's birth is imminent, which it may be, but it can also take up to an hour. It is hard work, but your partner and the midwife will be concentrating on supporting and helping you. The aim is for the baby's head to be born slowly enough to avoid tearing the perineum, which is the area of skin and muscle between the vagina and back passage. Sometimes tearing is unavoidable, or the midwife or doctor may ask your permission to do an episiotomy, which is basically cutting the skin to make the opening bigger. Afterwards, the cut or tear is stitched up and should heal without complications.

Once the baby's head is out the rest of the birth takes place fairly rapidly, and you can usually hold your child even before the cord is cut. She may be quite messy, covered with the white, greasy vernix which protects the skin in the womb and possibly some of your blood mixed in. (Throughout the book I shall refer to all children as 'she'; this is purely for ease of reference and stems from the fact that my two children so far have both been girls!) After a first quick cuddle, the staff will dry and weigh the baby, wrap her in a blanket and attach identification bracelets to wrist and ankle. Sometimes she will need a little extra attention, such as having mucus cleared from nose or mouth or being given some oxygen to enable proper breathing, but at this stage the priority is to get her back to you as quickly as possible, so mundane details like the first bath are left until much later on. This emphasis on helping you see your child as quickly as possible applies irrespective of the type of delivery, and whether the birth was aided by forceps, ventouse or Caesarian section, much of the procedure is standard. In each case everything will be explained very clearly, and the only possible scenario where you wouldn't be fully aware of what was going on would be if you had had to have a general anaesthetic.

Despite all the excitement, the third stage is still going on, and the placenta will be pushed out, usually speeded up by an injection in your thigh just after the baby is born. Any necessary stitching takes place, under a local anaesthetic if you haven't had an epidural, and you will be helped to wash and freshen up and taken to a recovery room. The traditional tea and toast is offered and greeted like a banquet, and you and your partner will be left alone with your baby for a while. This is an experience that stays with you for ever. You might both be exhausted, or as high as kites, or somewhere in between. It has been a long, long nine months, and you finally meet the person who caused it all. Nobody can predict how you might react, but every response is 'normal' and will have happened time and time again over the centuries. Relief that it is all over, a desperate urge to sleep, the desire to unwrap and examine this perfect little present – it could be anything.

For me, nothing could match the ecstasy of that first hour. When my first daughter was born, I felt I was meeting someone I recognised instantly and had been waiting for all my life. With my second, I apparently grinned inanely and continuously with sheer relief that I did in fact love her instantly, which had been my main concern from the moment of conception. On both occasions, I clearly remember that my husband and I talked inconsequential and utter rubbish to each other. It was simply lovely. You may find that the minute you see your baby the perfect name will simply pop into your head, but it can also take days and sometimes even weeks for it to come to you. You have six weeks in which to register the birth, which should be enough for anyone. Lay off the desire to name your child after an entire football team, unless you want to mortify the wee soul beyond belief.

The nurses will come back after a while, and you and your baby will be transferred to the ward. Again, this is a situation which is impossible to generalise about, so reactions will vary. Some women are utterly exhausted and fall asleep, while others spend the next 24 hours on a high which simply doesn't allow for a good snooze. Most maternity hospitals have little perspex cots which resemble unusual goldfish bowls but are ideal for viewing the new arrival from every angle and for hours at a time. Each ward has a secure nursery area, and the staff often recommend that the baby sleeps there for the first night, for a number of reasons. If you are exhausted, or on strong painkillers after a Caesarean section, you might be concerned that you won't hear the baby crying if she is next to you, while the observant and wide-awake night staff will be poised to respond to every whimper. Also, with your first baby in particular, it can be immensely reassuring to have an encouraging nurse helping you to breast feed successfully, and if they have actually brought a hungry baby to you then they are obviously going to make sure that you know what you are doing! However, if you really don't want your baby out of your sight then make that clear, but remember that you can always ask for help with feeding, irrespective of the time. Maternity hospitals offer 24-hour care everywhere, and a standard nine-to-five day is simply unheard of.

BREAST FEEDING

And so to feeding. We all know, and the research continues to tell us, time and again, that breast is best. That will never stop over-eager and cash-hungry formula producers from trying to persuade us otherwise. In my local maternity hospital, ready-made-up and free bottles of formula are constantly available for use, giving women a totally false impression about the ease and convenience of bottle feeding. You try sterilising, making up and heating eight bottles of milk in one go and you will start to realise what a handy attachment the boob actually is! The number of women who physically cannot breast feed is minuscule, and yet it is an excuse that is trotted out time and again.

However, speaking as someone suffering from the double handicap of chronic laziness and an older sister who was a breast-feeding counsellor, I never really considered any other option and launched into it with gay abandon. For a first-time mum I was incredibly lucky, as my daughter had apparently spent all her spare time in the womb learning to suck, and took to the whole procedure without a hint of a fuss. Second time round I gave birth to a biter, and my smugness evaporated post-haste. I had cracked and bleeding nipples, thrush and a few attacks of mastitis to put me firmly in my place.

In retrospect, I am now convinced that it is unfortunately some of the staunchest advocates of breast feeding who put other women off trying it. At no point in my first pregnancy was I told that breast feeding is often an acquired skill, but being aware of that would be sufficient for most women to keep persevering until they got it right. The first few days can be a nightmare, as your milk comes in and you find two enormous rugby balls where your perky boobs used to be. Your baby will occasionally take the lead and just get in there and suck, but most of them like a sort of guided tour before settling down to what is meant to be the most natural thing in the world. You have never done this before, and irrespective of the popular media images, simply being female does not automatically endow you with all the practicalities of childcare. Nobody would ever expect you to walk into any other job for which you had had no training and do it perfectly, so don't let anyone con you into the guilt trip which goes hand in hand with motherhood.

Once you get it right, breast feeding is a unique experience, and even the most reluctant can find themselves enthusiastically advocating it to all and sundry. The important thing here is getting it right, so don't be afraid to ask for help for as long as it takes. Maternity hospitals now have a pro-active policy to encourage breast feeding, and the staff are well trained, understanding and extremely encouraging. Probably more than most they are aware of the long-term health and development advantages brought about by breast feeding, and so from the medical aspect alone they will be eager to help. The National Childbirth Trust and La Leche League have branches throughout the country, and are ready to provide practical help and encouragement at any time, with particular emphasis on empathy. Usually you will find yourself talking to someone who has gone through an identical experience, which can be very comforting.

BREAST FEEDING PROBLEMS AND SOLUTIONS

There are lots of fancy modern remedies suggested for any of the initial physical side effects, but those who have gone through it all a few times seem to be united in recommending the traditional treatments, as follow. A good support bra is essential, although breast pads are an optional extra, as some women detest the feel of them. If you do decide to use them in the first few weeks there are a number of different kinds available, so shop around. Sore or cracked nipples respond well to a combination of fresh air and rubbing some of your own milk into the affected areas. A little heat treatment can also help, such as sitting bare chested in front of a fire, or using the medium setting on a hairdryer, although it is best not to dry out the skin too much.

Engorged breasts, which are usually hot and tender, can benefit from a soak in a warm bath or shower, where you also attempt to express a little milk and so relieve the pressure. If that fails, move on to the remedy which sounds like an April Fools' joke: chilled cabbage leaves. Keep the cabbage in the fridge and apply the leaves direct to your breasts underneath your bra and this will draw the heat out of the affected areas. As the leaves become warm and limp, replace them with fresh cold ones until your breasts recover. This sounds awful, works wonderfully and leaves you and your house smelling like a school dining-room. It is well worth it. If it doesn't work, however, it is time to contact your GP, as this could be a sign that mastitis has set in and antibiotics may be called for. Don't try to be brave and ignore mastitis, as it is a really horrid infection in the milk ducts which not only gives you localised pain but can make you feel as if you are in for a nasty bout of flu. Calendula cream is another homeopathic remedy for painful nipples, which can also double as treatment for nappy rash, dry skin or moisturiser when make-up is the last thing on your mind. If your precious infant has jaws like a pit bull, never make the mistake of yanking her off the breast as she will simply see this as a challenge and hang on grimly. Instead, ease your little finger into the side of her mouth to release the suction and gently move her from the nipple.

The medical world should, in theory, only contain experts, but the occasional half-wit will be tossed in to confuse you. Cunningly disguised as an intelligent health visitor or nurse – and usually childless and of the opinion that breast feeding is unnatural – they can undermine your confidence and come out with ridiculous pronouncements which convince you that bottle feeding is the only way to go. Their advice is usually along the lines of 'maybe you're not producing enough milk – you should top them up with a bottle' or 'you shouldn't lift them every time they cry – they're just looking for attention when they should be fed every four hours'. This is utter drivel. The more you feed, the more milk you produce. Similarly, breasts work along the laws of diminishing returns, and the less you use them, the less they produce. Furthermore, I don't know which dictator decided that a tiny, days-old baby was wilfully demanding attention. Babies cry because they need something; this is usually food, although the odd nappy change or cuddle is welcome. They have no concept of ruling your life; all they want is to satisfy their most basic needs. The fake experts think they know otherwise and delight in filling your head with garbage. Ignore them. If all else fails, get the most strident NCT counsellor you can find to out-talk them.

Breast feeding is quickly mastered, totally convenient and the best thing possible for your baby. Please give it a go, if only for the first six weeks, when it provides your baby with so many irreplaceable benefits. I can promise that once you have got the hang of it, nothing else comes close. On a purely practical note, breast-fed babies need no other liquids even in the warmest weather, don't get constipated and their nappies smell milky, rather than offensive in any way. You can breast feed discreetly anywhere, with no need for sterilising or reheating, and if you get really smart you can express half a pint a day to enable your partner to join in. It's true: breast is undoubtedly best.

The first few days of parenthood reveal gaping holes in your practical skills in relation to such basic things as bathing and dressing a newborn baby. In the hospital the nurses will be on hand to make sure you don't drop the darlings on their precious heads, but personal reactions to this sort of guidance are mixed. Grateful though you might be for all the attention and guidance, deep down you're desperate to get home and learn how to cope on your own. That doesn't necessarily mean that you have any confidence in yourself, but you have no choice. So the moment comes when you pack your bag, carefully collect all your cards and dress your baby in an immaculate going-home outfit. You have never been so nervous or excited in your life, but you try to act cool as you head on out into your brand new life as parents.

Chapter Three

Getting into the Swing of It

Every new mother comes home to a different situation regarding finances, available assistance and whether or not her partner is able to take some time off to help her. Some couples prefer to be by themselves, learning how to care for their baby without any extra help, while others cannot imagine life without Granny. Play it by ear, and don't be afraid to admit that you need a little help. Most women will already have experienced the 'three day blues' in hospital, where they get a bit weepy and generally feel down. For the majority this feeling is only short-lived, but some will suffer genuine post-natal depression, while others will be laid low by exhaustion, an inability to adjust or complete lack of time to relax. Post-natal depression needs professional help and must be regarded as the illness it undoubtedly is; trying to deal with it on your own can simply prolong the depression. You want to be able to enjoy your baby, so see your midwife or doctor and tell them exactly how you feel. The old taboos about depression are on the way out, and every area will have some sort of support group willing to listen and help.

Useful Help and Shortcuts

Tiredness is a killer. It wipes out fun, relaxation and concentration and, worst of all, you have no idea how you will cope with the new routine until you are right in the middle of it. Our lifesaver each time has been Granny, although it obviously helps if you have a good relationship to start with.

If your mother resembles a dictator with the sympathy levels of Idi Amin you are better off without her. What you need is someone who slips gently into the household routine, happy to eat dinner at midnight if that is when you all get round to it, and with the ability to keep everything ticking over without too much visible effort. After all, there is no point in wiping out the lady completely, when you want her to be a participating gran for years to come! Keep housework to the absolute minimum and meals extremely simple, try to space out your visitors a bit, and take every opportunity to have a peaceful shower or a 20-minute snooze. You will probably also notice that the busiest people offer the most help – please remember that they are the ones who know exactly what it is like and are totally sincere in their offers of help. By the time I had my first daughter, my sister-in-law had four children under ten. Despite this, she never – and still hasn't – offered advice I didn't ask for, for which I am immensely grateful, and turned up not only to admire the baby, but to do all my ironing. My baby was ten days old and had kept me up all night, and by this point I wasn't sure which end was which. That is the sort of help you want, and it is help which you will never forget.

Two or three weeks on, and a new pattern emerges. Your partner is back to work, Granny has gone home and you are on your own with your baby, trying to get to grips with all the things nobody had the decency to mention during your pregnancy. Although your community midwife gives up her daily visits, your tail end is making enough of a recovery to allow you to sit down from time to time, and breast feeding becomes easier by the day, there are still lots of other little details which you need to get used to. After delivery, you will continue to bleed for anything from two to six weeks, and while feeding in particular you will feel your womb contracting back to its normal size. This can be surprisingly uncomfortable, but often it will never have been mentioned so it comes as a bit of a shock. This is also a time when you feel very basic and close to nature as, irrespective of the number of baths or showers you have, you are very aware of all the most 'animal' fluids, such as blood and milk. I am always convinced that for three or four weeks you cannot get away from the earthiness of giving birth, if only because you become completely incapable of resembling anything human much before lunchtime. Show me a mother who has never found herself unwashed, uncombed and still in her dressing-gown at three o'clock in the afternoon, and I'll show you a mother with a full-time nanny.

It takes a while to realise that your baby's first priority is food. You might enjoy giving her a leisurely bath and dressing her up, but she really couldn't care less so long as she can smell your milk. Some babies actively dislike being bathed, which is pretty disappointing when you contemplate your colour-coordinated baby bath, accessories and towels. Nappy-changing boxes are handy, because they keep everything together and are easily transportable throughout the house, as are changing bags for when you actually get round to getting out of the house. Newborn babies use so many nappies that it is almost impossible to generalise about the benefits of one brand over another, so go for cheap until they start moving about a bit more and you can justify the expense of the quality brands. You can save a fair bit by buying in bulk, and make use of the money-off coupons which will arrive through the post with amazing regularity.

When you were pregnant you probably had the occasional fantasy of gliding down the street, pushing your brand new pram with your delightful infant sleeping peacefully inside. The same dream might have included a perfectly made-up, svelte you, an immaculate house and a delicious dinner simmering in the oven, because you would have so much time on your hands with maternity leave and an angelic child. Let's dispel these myths one at a time. If you don't slap on make-up the minute you crawl out of bed, the chances are that your shiny, possibly unwashed face will remain unadorned until bedtime. Breast feeding will undoubtedly burn up the calories, but toned, firm flesh doesn't come naturally to the majority of new mothers. If you can find, and have the discipline to stick to, a good home workout video, that's fine, but check out your maternity hospital for post-natal facilities before forking out large sums of money to use a trendy gym. Many clinics encourage you to come along for six or eight weeks of fitness classes, and also make allowances for you to bring your babies, which is something 'Shape up with Superfit Sue' is apt to forget. Thereafter, look at local authority fitness centres; they vary from place to place, but most aim to provide a good range of fitness classes at reasonable prices, along with crèche facilities. Remember that you are not as restricted by time as you were while working, and there is no rule to say that you can't leave the house looking like a bombsite for a couple of hours while you attempt to regain your pre-pregnancy figure.

Having your house in this condition can leave some of us completely unmoved, while others are unable to settle until the worst of the debris is tackled. You alone know what you can comfortably live with, but in the early days you will have to make some sort of compromise when you realise that you simply cannot do it all. Get into the habit of a quick whisk around morning and night to get rid of the most obvious mess – it is amazing how emptying bins, folding newspapers and stacking dirty dishes can give some semblance of tidiness! You won't find this on the usual list of required items when baby arrives, but I would put my money – and I know it is quite a lot of money – on a dishwasher. We didn't have one when daughter No. 1 arrived, and we seemed to spend an awful lot of time scrubbing food-encrusted crockery. Before the arrival of No. 2 we moved house, and since we were already spending huge amounts of cash with gay abandon, we succumbed to my mum's advice and splashed out on a fine specimen. We became very close very quickly, and I have to admit to loving my dishwasher in a manner I thought impossible with a household machine. Evenings with the new baby were far easier than first anticipated, as we sat down to leisurely meals secure in the knowledge that it would then take all of five minutes to make the kitchen look reasonably tidy.

The delicious-dinners fantasy rapidly disappears under a stream of TV dinners, supplemented by the local chip shop. Our two main standbys have been soup and pasta. Either jazz up tinned or packet soup with some imaginative ingredients, or get into the habit of flinging every vegetable known to man into a pot every couple of days, along with the stock cube of your choice. Minestrone soup, which everyone makes a different version of, is a really filling meal if you toss some pasta into it and serve it with crusty bread. Pasta is unbeatable. I don't know what to recommend in its place if you don't like it, because it usually satisfies every taste. Best of all, if the thought of whipping up your own sauce couldn't be further from your mind, every supermarket and corner shop has the most amazing variety in dried, tinned and fresh versions. Many of them freeze well and don't take up much space, and the same goes for the appropriate rolls or baguettes to go with them. Add a salad, which it is possible to make while breast feeding (although care is recommended), and you have the perfect tasty, nutritious and filling meal. Try and stay away from stodgy or sweet puddings, and stick to fresh fruit and yoghurts. (However, I have got a real nerve saying this, as I have a sweet tooth and could happily eat for Scotland, but although the results didn't show too badly the first time, four months after my second child was born I was still two stone overweight.)

Life will settle down into a manageable routine, but when it comes to necessary chores go easy on yourself for the first three months. If money allows, it can be a tremendous boost to get your house cleaned from top to bottom once in a blue moon, and the ironing can be dealt with in the same way. Our local laundrette will iron 40 items for £10, which is a very sound investment, and one which is no doubt available countrywide. Sadly, a lot of morale-boosting is cash-related, but a chance to relax and get your hair done is sometimes worth far more than the money you actually pay. Baby-swopping with a friend or sister is another excellent way to allow you both a couple of hours to pamper yourself. I hate to sound shallow, but there is something very uplifting about concentrating totally on yourself for once, and the prospect of painting your nails without interruptions becomes positively exciting! Grabbing sleep wherever and whenever is a must, and there is a great deal to be said for ignoring any chores on a wet afternoon, and instead spending the time curled up on the couch with an equally dozy infant.

Babies' sleep patterns differ dramatically, as do parental reactions. What sort of sleeper you end up with comes down to pure luck, as there is little or no chance of any sort of sustainable habit-training possible in the first five or six months. Some will work on the recognised night/day routine from the word go, while others will take some time to adjust. I am not going to depress anyone by quoting the accepted statistics of the amount of sleep the average newborn needs, as I don't know any babies who have actually read the book or follow the guidelines. Adults can consult statistics as much as they like, but they cannot affect them. If you do come up with a foolproof, safe method of getting your baby to sleep when you want her to, then I suggest you patent it – as you will be about to make a fortune.

GROWTH SPURTS

All breast-feeding babies have a regular, delightful habit which few people will tell you about until you are right in the middle of it all. This is known as growth spurts, and it works entirely on the theory of supply and demand. Every so often, usually beginning when children are ten days old and continuing until after they have started school, that sophisticated computer also known as the child's brain tells her body that it is time she grew a bit. This is extremely straightforward when you have reached a point where the child can simply ask for a cheese sandwich or a second helping of pudding, but it takes you by surprise when your tiny baby starts eating non-stop.

The principle behind this is beautifully simple: your baby needs to up her supply of milk and the only way to tell your body to come up with the goods is to breast feed more or less constantly until milk production matches requirements. This can be really daunting for a new mum, but it has to be said that this is mainly because most of us are sadly unprepared for this event. Each baby's favoured way of feeding through a growth spurt is different from that of the next, although for some unknown reason my children preferred to feed literally all night – and no, I never worked out if they had perfected the art of drinking in their sleep – and sleep peacefully for most of the following day. Three long nights and dazed days later I would be producing enough milk to rival the dairy down the road, while the bags under my eyes would have provided room for enough holiday clothes for a family of four.

On a more serious note, the first time I went through this my main feelings were a bewildering mixture of inadequacy, exhaustion and worry that I wasn't producing enough milk to satisfy my baby. Had it not been for the care of an NCT breast-feeding counsellor I would have been easy prey for that nightmare health professional: the misinformed health visitor. There are some fine health visitors around, but at the risk of causing a huge outcry I have to say that every mother I have spoken to has also encountered the sort of person who shouldn't be allowed near a vulnerable group such as new mums. The following scenario sums up inadequate health visitors.

My younger sister and I had our children fairly close together, but our first-born couldn't have been more different physically. Her son was a wiry young man who immediately set his life time patterns by eating constantly but never becoming remotely chubby. Meanwhile, while my daughter is now the same kind of slender build, she spent the first six months of her life getting rounder and rounder. Both children were breast fed exclusively for six months and were obviously very contented, but neither of our health visitors was happy, because neither child fitted the average statistics. My sister was accused of underfeeding her baby, and advised to supplement his feeds with a bottle, while 12 miles away my health visitor was asking me if I was giving my child sweets or chocolate – she was ten weeks old at this point! – and suggesting that I cut back on her breast feeds. All the advice was not only misleading, it was actually wrong. You cannot overfeed a breast-fed baby, and it is extremely rare to underfeed one, although if that were a possibility you should just be shown how to up your milk production.

My sister and I were both left feeling very uncomfortable, with lingering doubts about how well we were shaping up as first-time mums. However, a quick chat with our midwife mum left us in no doubt that we were each doing the right thing for our own baby, and any further nonsensical suggestions were treated with the disdain they deserved. Try to make sure that you are as well informed as possible over vital issues like feeding, and it helps to have a reassuring contact point like your community midwife or surgery nurse, whom you can trust to be encouraging and supportive.

EXPRESSING MILK

If you are considering expressing milk for your baby, it is a good idea to start as early as four or five weeks, so the baby learns to use a bottle from time to time. For such tiny people babies can be very determined, and it is amazing how well they make their preferences known. They have a valid point. On the one hand, they can snuggle against their favourite person, cushioned by a warm, soft breast which produces the perfect drink at the perfect temperature. The other option involves a much harder teat dispensing milk from some solid object smelling of disinfectant. Well, which would you prefer? Expressing milk is like riding a bike – once you have got the knack it is never forgotten, but learning involves much trial and error. There are various methods, ranging from hand expressing to electric or battery-operated machines, but relaxation is the key to success.

Breast milk comes in two parts, beginning with the fore-milk, which is the lighter thirst-quencher, and then moving on to the creamy hind-milk, which provides the real calories. Perhaps the best time to begin is after feeding your baby from one side, so she is totally satisfied, while you are still in feeding mode. One very handy tip is to sit in a warm bath, so you are relaxed and comfortable. I finally cracked the procedure by putting a happily gurgling baby in her cot next to the bath, and chatting to her while I tried to relax as much as possible. Eventually, I realised that expressing very slowly produced the best results, and went from half a dozen drops to eight ounces within a week. As I became more confident I speeded up, and finally reached a point where I automatically expressed four to six ounces twice a day at the end of a normal feed. This was frozen in sterile bottles, with the date clearly marked on them. If you do this early enough, it is quite easy to persuade your baby to take a bottle from time to time, and it is a good idea to make it part of the daily routine. It is also an opportunity for your partner to get really involved in feeding, especially if he always gives the same feed at around the same time every day.

If you find expressing too time-consuming or impossible to get to grips with using the standard equipment, your local NCT should have a contact for hiring an electric breast pump. Using this successfully is all that is usually needed to convince the least-confident woman that she can master expressing on her own, and there is then an easy transition back to the original method. Continuing to feed your baby in this way is now extremely popular, which is reflected in the range of products available to facilitate the ongoing use of breast milk, especially for women returning to work long before they wish to consider weaning. Modern breast pumps are light and easily transportable, and you can choose from a wide range of containers to transport the fruits of your efforts. Make it quite clear in your workplace that you would like regular use of somewhere private and clean – and definitely NOT the toilet – and the response is likely to be very positive. One of my friends found the staunchest ally in her managing director, who vacated his comfortable office for her every day at lunchtime and made sure there was space in his chilled drinks cabinet for her precious bottles of milk. His only proviso was that the bottles were always clearly marked, so that his slightly dotty secretary didn't serve up the milk with his clients' coffee!

EARLY EXPEDITIONS

In the carefree days BC (Before Children), you nipped out at the drop of a hat, with your only concern being whether or not a brolly was required. Now, in addition to the method of transport used by the baby, you could do with a packhorse to carry all the vital equipment. Keep a changing bag ready by the front door, and check the contents regularly. Apart from nappies, wipes and cream, the essentials are a change of clothing – sometimes two, if you have one of these talented little darlings who can erupt from both ends at any given moment – and a couple of indispensable muslin nappies, which can be put to a multitude of uses. If you do get caught short, places like Mothercare and the Early Learning Centre will come to your rescue, so don't be afraid to ask.

Try and make sure that you live in a child-friendly area, although this is usually outwith your control, and if you are planning a holiday or a break in this country, find out about changing and feeding facilities before booking up. My husband and I spent our honeymoon in St Andrews, which is a fabulous place for a couple, but unless things change radically we will not be returning until our children have reached some recognisable stage of civilisation. Maybe they don't like babies there, or they think nappies don't need changing or little faces feeding, but at the moment of writing there wasn't a single place in the main street which allowed you to do either.

Most city centres can provide some basic facilities, but I haven't yet discovered a shopping centre, restaurant or café which can match the big child-orientated shops. My least favourite places are the few shops with 'no prams or buggies' notices. It is your duty to struggle into these places, pile up the shopping and when told that you cannot bring in your pram, abandon it all with cries of horror. Choose ringing tones, enlist the help of every other customer in the place and decry the society we live in which cannot encourage the safety and care of our children. Leave in high dudgeon and write an anguished letter to your local paper. None of it might help in the slightest, but it doesn't half make you feel better!

Baby slings and carriers provide the simplest method of travelling light. Practise at home first, until you can slide the baby in and out easily, and remember not to overdress her, as she will be able to use your body heat. This is a very intimate way to travel, and can also help you feel that you get about with the minimum of fuss. Wear a jacket with an accessible pocket for cash or cheque book, sling a small rucksack-type bag on your back and away you go. This method is also best used in conjunction with sensible shoes rather than stilettos, for obvious reasons.

ANXIETY

No matter how much you wanted a baby, or longed to be at home caring for your child, there are times when the reality will be hard going. There will be moments of the purest happiness, when the two of you just gaze at each other, or you watch your baby sleeping in the middle of the night and know that this is the best thing you have ever done. But there will always be moments when the pressures of responsibility will rob you of your enjoyment, and leave you biting your nails with anxiety. The terror of something bad happening is at the back of every parent's mind, although most of us deal with this as practically as possible by taking every sensible step to keep the child safe. Your hospital or clinic will give you relevant leaflets about caring for your baby, and although they can vary depending on where you live, the one piece of information given to everyone concerns the prevention of cot death, or Sudden Infant Death Syndrome as it is also known.

It is hard to put this into perspective. The advice is vital for every parent as it actively reduces the risk of cot death, but it is a difficult subject to contemplate and leaves many parents panicking. Current research advises that you always put babies to sleep on their backs, avoid dressing them too warmly or overheating the room, and do not smoke or allow others to smoke near them. This cannot be emphasised too strongly. While research to clarify the exact cause of cot death is ongoing, cigarette smoke has already been identified as the cause of coughs, asthma and chest infections in babies and young children. If your baby is unwell and you are at all concerned seek medical advice, irrespective of the time of day or night. It can take some time for parental instinct to develop fully, but the average nurse or GP is very sympathetic when it comes to the worries of brand new parents, and are apt to encourage your enquiries rather than ignore them. Fortunately stroppy receptionists are becoming a rarer breed, but if you feel that they are trying to put you off when you have a legitimate concern, remain polite but very firm and insist on speaking to the doctor. You can outlast them, so just stay calm and keep repeating your request over and over again until they crumble.

Assuming that you are on maternity leave, you are obviously going to have more time to get to know your baby and get into a proper routine than your partner is. However, don't merely assume that he has just gone straight back into the pre-baby days without any of the changes that you are facing. Perhaps the fathers of the past left everything to mother but times have certainly changed. Selective night-time deafness still appears to be an affliction borne by some dads, but the majority are more likely to be offering a helping hand, even in situations where their presence is not absolutely necessary. Having said that, sharing all the little trials and tribulations of the first few weeks can make for an unforgettable experience, and even the tiredest, most harassed and grumpiest new mum will remember her partner's contribution and involvement for the rest of her life. Before the baby actually arrives, make a deal with each other that no matter how tired or fed up you get, you will make a positive effort not to take it out on each other. It sounds simple enough, but putting it into action takes real effort. However, the rewards are immeasurable.

Instead of biting his head off the minute he walks through the door, give him the baby to entertain while you make a desperately needed cup of tea, or gin and tonic. Tell each other that you would like half an hour for an uninterrupted bath or to read the paper, and then swop over. I am quite sure that you never communicated telepathically before you became parents, so I don't know where you get the time to acquire such a refined skill the minute the baby arrives. Even if you have the easiest child in the world, be kind to each other and have the good manners to say 'thanks'. If he keeps you company in the middle of the night and does the nappy change so you can get back to sleep, let him know that it is very much appreciated. Similarly, if he is full of praise for the way you are coping or amazed how quickly you have become expert at the nappy changes or bathing, then have a well-deserved little glow at your achievements.

I once read an interview with a woman who had deliberately had a child on her own, as none of her relationships had worked out. She said the hardest thing about being a lone parent was that there was no one else in the world as besotted by or interested in her child as she was, and she felt that had to be one of the great sustaining strengths of a good relationship. I found that a really poignant remark, which summed up the best of parenthood for me. At the end of the day, you can drive friends, family and colleagues demented with tales of your perfect offspring, but after an initial forgivable rush I suggest you keep the bulk of it for your equally mesmerised partner. Try to have a little time alone together, even if it is just for a couple of hours in the pub where you catch up on life with each other. However, don't be surprised if you spend your first few nights out just talking about the baby. It might be boring, it's certainly predictable, but it's undoubtedly normal.

RESUMING A SEX LIFE

Hand in hand with talk of relationships comes the six-week check-up, where your doctor might ask if you have resumed a sexual relationship. Resist the temptation to gape at him open-mouthed and say: 'Sex? What's sex? Oh yes, that's what got me into this state in the first place.' At our postnatal get-together, one of the girls airily informed the rest of us that the day she got home from hospital she put the baby to sleep and celebrated with a bottle of champagne and a lengthy love-making session with her husband. The rest of us were totally stunned, if admittedly a little envious, and there was much wincing and crossing of legs, while the class wit summed up the majority feeling by muttering: 'You'd have had to knock me unconscious with the bottle before I'd have contemplated it!'

Don't be pressured by this feeling that everything springs back to normal immediately. It doesn't help that the day after delivery you think a practical joke is being played on you when some grinning idiot pops up beside your bed and brightly asks what contraception you plan to use. Do not hit this person. Let her rabbit on and leave all her informative little leaflets, but this is not the time to read them. Take them home and put them somewhere handy like your underwear drawer, so that when you stop wearing baggy bloomers and move back to your slinkies you pick the right moment to consider sex.

We have all heard the stories of women who turn up pregnant at their six-week check-up, and some of us have even met them, but this is not standard procedure. Resuming a sex life is a very personal choice, but try and bear in mind that for many women the first time after giving birth is almost a test to see if they can still do it, rather than a truly erotic experience. Usually, the realisation that the basics remain the same and that this is still a fun way of relaxing and enjoying yourself is enough to get you right back into the swing of things, but some couples don't find it quite so straightforward. It is tempting to ignore any discomfort and abandon sex altogether, especially if other pressures mean that it is no longer high on your list of priorities. However, any medical problem arising as a direct result of giving birth can be dealt with quickly and painlessly, but the longer any treatment is left the harder it can become to go and ask for help.

Similarly, if you find it so difficult to relax that intercourse is painful or downright impossible, the experts recommend that rather than abandoning your sex life, you approach it from a completely different angle. Agree to leave penetrative sex off the agenda for some time and concentrate on pleasuring each other in other ways. It sounds really obvious, but works beautifully once the pressure is off, and long before you anticipated it your sex life is back to normal – and often far better than before. Ignore all the prophets of doom who claim that the arrival of children signifies the end of an enjoyable adult relationship and let them sort out their own hang-ups. However, there is one question which comes up time and time again: is it true that all babies have an in-built radar which encourages them to scream for attention at the most delicate of moments? Sorry, but it certainly looks that way, and nobody has yet come up with a half-decent solution.

CRYING

To my mind, I have left the worst till last in my description of the first few weeks. You can cope with anything if there are moments of peace and tranquillity, and a chance to appraise your new life, but this is well-nigh impossible if you end up with a baby who cries constantly. This is the most frustrating of situations, especially if you go for help and none of the experts can tell you why your child refuses to settle, apart from the possibility that she may have colic. Often referred to as 'three-month colic', this is an awful affliction for all concerned. The baby can be well fed, changed and to all intents and purposes as comfortable as it is possible for a baby to be, yet cries continuously. This crying is often at its worst in the evening, when you and your partner are also tired, hungry and tense. A baby crying is designed to alert her parents to respond to her needs, but being unable to calm a child can drive anyone to distraction. Assuming that your child has been checked by the doctor and there are no signs of illness, all you can do is follow some basic practical tips on getting through each night and day until the magical three month-milestone.

CRY-SIS has to be your first stop, if only because they will put you in touch with a local counsellor who has experienced the same difficulties. They will pass on any tips that members have found helpful and there are recommended procedures or checklists which help you feel in some control of this frustrating situation. If you have considered all the possibilities such as hunger, wind or discomfort and discounted them, you can try soothing movement. Being rocked in your arms or carried in a sling may help a baby in distress, as may a walk in the pram or a run in the car. Sucking can comfort, so a dummy can be of use in some cases. Make sure it is sterilised and resist all temptation to dip it in something sweet.

If you find yourself reaching screaming point, put the baby safely down in its cot or pram. Never, ever shake children in an attempt to shock them into stopping crying. This can cause brain damage. Put some music on and go into another room, or stand at the back door for ten minutes until you calm down. Phone your CRY-SIS contact, the Samaritans or someone close to you who understands what you are going through. This will not last for ever. Give the baby to your mum or a close friend, and get out for an hour from time to time, or go to bed for a while. At the weekends, make sure you and your partner take turnabout so you both get some sort of a break. This is a soul-destroying experience which nobody could face calmly, but the strangest thing about it is that one day you will wake up and it will have just stopped. And in the same way that nobody could tell you why it started, no one can tell you why it ended. Take a deep breath, congratulate yourselves on getting through it and enjoy your baby, who will now probably turn into the most sunny-tempered little person imaginable.

When you look at the first three months of life as a parent you are considering the most enormous upheaval, and although it appears that I am presenting you with a list of woes, they are nothing compared to the good bits. It can be really daunting to read some of the pregnancy manuals, which carry you smoothly through the nine months, even serve you well in the labour room, and then leave you with a great, fat nothing. Although a first pregnancy in particular is all-consuming in the most indulgent way, it is simply a lead-up to your starring role as a parent.

We no longer have the family network systems of days gone by, for a number of reasons, and most of us could do with a little help from time to time, especially when it comes to receiving hints of possible or common problems. The most ghoulish old wives' tales are being laid to rest, and that can only be beneficial, but many of the best traditions and remedies still hold good and hopefully will always be passed on. Hope for the best, expect the worst, and remember that there are an awful lot of us who go on to do it again and again, so it can't be that bad. If you have at least some idea of the hiccups that can crop up from time to time, even the knowledge that you are not alone can be enough to keep you going. By the time your baby is three months old you won't believe how practised, relaxed and confident you are – in fact, you might even have the occasional minute when you think you're a pretty good parent! And there will always be moments with your baby which are so tender and uplifting that you would hesitate to share them, but they fulfil everything and more that you had hoped for when you first started thinking about having a child. They come out of the blue and make up for everything that irritates you. Imagine looking out over a peaceful night, holding a well-fed and contented bundle who is murmuring herself to sleep against your neck, and try and think about any of the disadvantages to having this little person. Tomorrow morning you might curse yourself for your sentimentality, but for now, nothing else matters.

Chapter Four

Health and Fitness: Yours

There comes a point when your new life begins to follow a recognisable pattern, and you start to notice tiny details. These are mainly personal, and usually very unflattering. Your partner looks relatively unchanged, your child is quite simply gorgeous, but there is one jarring note in this family scene: you. Some women spend their pregnancy exercising caution when it comes to putting on weight and getting out of shape, others are too nauseous to contemplate excess food, while the luckiest of all spend their entire pregnancies pigging out and then find that breast feeding removes all that unsightly blubber within six weeks. They are always the ones who come to the antenatal class reunion in full war paint and size 8 jeans, and chatter happily about how the weight 'simply slipped off'. Resist the temptation to put them out of your misery with a hard slap. The sad truth is that while a lucky few spring back into shape almost immediately after giving birth, the majority of us face motherhood with all the over-indulgence of the last nine months making itself rather too well known on waistline and hips.

Assuming that you are one of the poor souls who cannot look at their body without bursting into tears and reaching for a large bar of comforting chocolate, where do you start? First of all, forget unrealistic expectations. Stretch marks will not fade overnight, irrespective of the exotic lotions you might rub into them, but will eventually fade to silvery, thread-like traces which you will be able to live with. Dry skin can be treated fairly quickly as long as you find the time to slap on moisturiser, and it also helps to chuck a couple of drops of baby oil in your bath. (Make sure you clean it out afterwards, before you and your partner discover the thrills of skating on oil in a very enclosed space!)

One rather unsightly condition can appear on your knees, where you develop thick, scaly patches of skin. This is not a mysterious and possibly incurable disease, but a direct result of spending hours kneeling on the floor changing nappies. Move to an upright position, always making sure your baby cannot take a header to the floor, and this ugly complaint will disappear pronto. Your crowning glory can become another source of woe, as you find yourself moulting huge clumps of hair all over the place. Part of the reason for this is that during pregnancy you do not lose the normal amount of hair, and can become rather lush and hirsute as a result. Then your body simply starts making up for lost time, but leaves you convinced that baldness is just around the corner. If you are convinced that your hair is rapidly becoming overthin then see your doctor, but any such condition is normally very short-lived.

Food Fads

And so to the body beautiful, and don't you wish it was! Once you decide that you want to be slim and fit again, the temptation is to go a bit mad and starve yourself. If you have previously spent a great deal of time, energy and rightful pride in looking slim, fit and gorgeous, then suddenly starting to feel like the lazy, fat slobs you always looked at with such scorn can be devastating. Slow down before you do anything drastic, and consider your diet to start with. Diets don't work, be they faddy grapefruit-and-hard-boiled-eggs numbers, or scientific-sounding schemes like The Miami Institute System, where your main meal consists of ice-cream and green beans. To my everlasting shame, I have to admit that the reason I know they don't work is because I have tried most of them. I have also tried closing my eyes and simply wishing the blubber away, starving myself for two or three days, and pretending I don't care what I look like. None of these is a reasonable solution.

Eating sensibly, boring though it is, is the only guaranteed way of reducing weight, but you have to be in the right frame of mind before attempting a long-term eating plan. Speaking as the sort of idiot who ate myself into a stupor during my first pregnancy, managed to lose most of it a year later and regained it all and more during my second pregnancy, I have to say that this is not the way to become fit and happy. A year after my second daughter was born I weighed two and a half stone more than when I got married, and then lost a stone before becoming pregnant for the third time. This left me in the unenviable position of having to make sure that I gained no more than a few pounds throughout the entire nine months, and I wouldn't recommend that to anyone. Having said all that, there is a world of difference between being a few pounds curvier than previously and loving your new look, and being a walking advertisement for a well-fitting marquee!

So how do you begin? Most antenatal clinics will have handed out good eating plans, and following them is as good a way as any for kicking off. The key to long-term success is to remember that this is not a diet. As such, you are allowed the occasional bit of what you fancy without then falling into the classic dieter's trap of chomping your way through the biscuit barrel because you have 'ruined it all anyway'. If you go out to dinner and spend the entire evening flirting with the crème caramel, then give in and live a little. This is not some rigid regime where you're punished for indulging yourself, but rather a way of life which allows and even encourages the odd hint of luxury.

To complicate matters further, the chances are high that as

a breast-feeding mother you will have developed an appetite which leaves you stunned by its ferocity. Never mind three square meals a day, you want six and you want them now. This is another of nature's cunning little ways of ensuring the continuation of the species, and for some considerable time your main function will appear to be consuming and then passing on copious amounts of calories. This is serious eating, not to be diverted by mere snacks. The problem is exacerbated when you're too tired, harassed or busy to make a healthy plateful of food, and succumb instead to crisps, sweets or biscuits. These give an instant lift, but aren't long lasting, so in no time at all your body is demanding real food again and all the extras turn into fat.

Complicated eating plans fall quickly into disuse. Eat plenty of fresh fruit and vegetables, adding tinned or frozen when convenient, and go for carbohydrate with every meal. Bread, potatoes, rice, pasta and cereals fill you up and are an important source of vitamins and fibre. On a daily basis, include lean meat, fish, eggs, cheese, beans or lentils, and remember the importance of dairy products. These need not be excessively fatty, as you can get low-fat varieties of most of them. Some foods are very good for you in your postnatal condition, such as green, leafy vegetables and dried fruit and nuts, all of which contain iron. To help absorb iron you need vitamin C, which is found in citrus fruit, tomatoes, broccoli, blackcurrants and potatoes. Cut right down on sugary food and drinks, and drink lots of water. Similarly, accept that you actually need very little fat, and remember that it is not just the fry-ups which are laden in fat, but that pastries, chocolate and biscuits contain a surprisingly large amount. If you like to take vitamin supplements, check first of all with your GP who will advise which are best to take while breast feeding.

Now for an incentive. Imagine yourself spending months of boredom on an endless round of miserable diets where you lose some, gain some and essentially stay the same. Now imagine the same length of time eating pleasurably, if not piggishly, and emerging at the end of it all in just the healthy shape you would like to be. If you are childish, like me, you will feel that regular rewards are in order. Put aside any money you would normally spend on snacks or sweets, and buy exotic out-of-season fruit for a treat, or luxuries such as smoked salmon or caviar where you can literally only afford a couple of bites. Best of all, hoard your pennies for ages and buy a bottle of champagne to share with your beloved. You have to eat something delicate and light with it, so a steak and kidney pie would never do, while lemon sole or a dainty chicken dish would be perfect. Champagne has a very interesting effect on some people, so you might find that not only are you consuming fewer calories, but you get involved in some unexpected exercise as well!

EXERCISE

If only all exercise was as much fun. All the good girls will have listened to the physiotherapists in the hospital and started their postnatal exercises as soon as they were fit enough, taking into account discomforts such as stitches or Caesarean sections. They do work, but again it all comes down to regularity and dedication. Even the top stars and supermodels who regain their figures four weeks after giving birth are quick to point out that none of it sprung back into place through magic. It is obviously a bit easier if you have a personal trainer, a full-time nanny to care for your baby while you work out, and an income which depends on you remaining lithe and lovely at all times. Even the women who become professional mothers, dragging their children on to early-morning television or down catwalks at the drop of a cheque book, make sure that they remain confident in their looks. It is depressing for the rest of us, and the best way to deal with it is by catty remarks about these women being so obsessed by themselves that they are useless mothers – but that is also a rather unreasonable attitude. The most likely explanation for these gorgeous creatures still looking exquisite while juggling baby, job and home is that they have managed to get their routine down to a fine art, and religiously follow an exercise plan, no matter how often they have been up in the night. They are nearly always the same ones who never miss a deadline, turn up late for work or look like the wreck of the Hesperus just because they haven't slept for a week.

The only way to fitness is to exercise regularly, and yet this concept of having some time to yourself is alien to most parents, especially first-timers. However, there are shortcuts. If you are looking for a stomach as hard as a washboard and thigh muscles to match, you are going to have to put aside some time every day to concentrate on the relevant exercises. Get some music on, put your baby in a seat and position where she can watch you, and go for it. There are even some lovely books and manuals which encourage you to exercise with your baby, which isn't as mad as it sounds. Your baby is just enjoying a crane, or 'king of the castle', on top of your legs, and meanwhile you are experiencing the sort of inner-thigh stretch which you would pay a fortune for in an exclusive health club.

Aerobic exercise is a different matter, and the experts recommend at least three 20-minute sessions a week to get your heart going, a bit of sweat broken and your muscles moving noticeably. Don't throw your hands in the air in horror at the thought of fitting this into your already bursting schedule before you have a good look at your normal daily routine. The chances are that you already spend a good part of your day doing one of the best forms of aerobic exercise – walking. Pushing a pram or buggy gives you tremendous momentum, and it is something you can get into in a big way, especially with your first baby. Remember that second time around you will have a reluctant toddler in tow, whose idea of a brisk walk is meandering around a play park, so make the most of it. Once you get used to it, you will find that you cover surprising distances.

Initially, your baby will probably lie quietly, or sleep, but as children get older there is nothing they like better than to be propped up, watching the world go by. Dry weather makes hiking around easier, but most prams and buggies have excellent raincovers which withstand the worst downpours. Suitably clad yourself you can hit the road in all weathers except gale-force winds, unless you have Mary Poppins aspirations. I always use prams and buggies which face me, because my children enjoy a good gab as we stroll along, and it is rather pleasant to spend hours beaming at your favourite little face, all animated and excited with the big world out there. Some prefer to let their children face outwards, so they can see more of the great horizons; it is very much a matter of personal choice.

All you need now are the facilities for regular pit-stops, and you will very quickly become acquainted with the best places to feed or to change a nappy. Sometimes the less obvious places are the most welcoming; for instance, we have a very child-friendly policy in our city libraries, and as a result you can nip in with your pram and be made to feel very much at home. There is a real feeling of relaxation in stopping after a two-hour walk, curling into a comfortable chair with your baby and a good book or magazine, and just unwinding for half an hour. Most libraries will also give you the use of the disabled toilet facilities to change your baby, and they are normally spacious and well kept. Maybe it is not the trendiest way of keeping fit and improving your mind at the same time, but for sheer enjoyment it is hard to beat.

Maybe this all sounds a little too humdrum and mumsy,

and you crave some time to yourself. Council sports centres usually offer the best value for money, although you can sometimes have membership of a club as a job perk. The range of exercises should have something to suit everyone, from circuit training to swimming. Again, the key to success is sticking to regular workouts, so it might be an idea to book and pay in advance; it can really focus your mind when you are tempted to give up but have already shelled out the cash. If you choose something fairly strenuous make sure that you ease yourself in gently, and if your instructor is of the 'no pain, no gain' school of thought, get out fast before you do some serious damage. You need to build up strength and stamina slowly, or you will give up in disgust. Once your baby has had all necessary injections you can go swimming as a family, and you can do some serious breaststroke while your partner plays with the baby. Another family exercise which you can all get involved in is cross-country walking, as the only extras you will need will be a baby sling or carrier of some description, and a small rucksack to carry the nappy paraphernalia.

SOCIALISING WITH OTHER PARENTS

You have now changed your diet and taken up some useful pursuit to stretch your body, so is there anything else you need to enrich your life? Well, yes, but it is something that is easily overlooked when you think about maternity leave or being a stay-at-home mum. No matter how much you love your baby or adore your new way of life, you reach a point where a little adult company is extremely welcome. You can do this the smart way, as I did, and have your first baby at the same time as two of your sisters and half a dozen friends. Despite all the speculation, we did not synchronise our husbands, but it made things so much easier as we all struggled to cope with our new role in life. About a year before this baby boom, one of my friends had her baby first, and found it a very isolating experience. Everyone else was probably toying with the idea, but the reality of this was that we were all still immersed in house-buying, careers and socialising, while this one poor couple felt that they were heading off in a new direction all by themselves. Even maternity leave wasn't much fun for my friend, as she had no one to while away the hours with, and after the baby arrived and her husband went back to work she found the time very long and lonely, despite thoroughly enjoying spending time with her daughter.

If this is your situation, try to plan ahead while you are pregnant, and consider the other women in your antenatal class as potential friends. Keep in touch with those you get on well with, and you will find that this sort of socialising has a knock-on effect. Some of these women will possibly have older children, so they will already be familiar with mother-and-toddler groups and point you in the right direction. When you have a very young baby it is tempting to think of these groups as being only for older children, but bear in mind that they can also be of benefit to parents and give you a good chance to meet people in similar situations. Even a baby of three or four months can start to enjoy the whirl of activity generated by a crowd of toddlers, and will happily watch everything going on until old enough to join in. The familiarity can also be very comforting as the children move on to different situations and discover how many children they know within their particular area; when my first daughter started school I realised that she had classmates she had played with since she was less than a year old.

The format for these groups runs along similar lines wherever you are. You pay a certain amount to join the group for a year, with the money going towards toys, use of the hall and any other incidental expenses, and then pay a small amount every week which covers the cost of tea, coffee, juice and biscuits. Unless you are part of a super-organised crowd who actually employ someone to do the chores, you will have a rota system of determining who is on duty to take out toys and tidy them away, make coffee and clear up. Part of the fun is helping the children make something, be it a picture or a puppet, and usually there will be two or three people excused the usual rota on the understanding that they organise these crafts. Fundraising events are common, as are nights out at Christmas or just whenever you feel the need to socialise. It can be quite daunting to attempt to join what appears to be a well-established group, but most of the women already there will have felt the same way, and if you can summon up the first deep breath and say 'Hello, I'm Blah and this is my baby Gurgles' you will be part of the crowd before you know it.

Don't expect to like everyone; there will always be someone whose ideas on life, parenting and the world at large are so different from yours that you wonder if you are on the same planet. Similarly, don't be intimidated by an officious committee, because it is a sad fact of life that some people are unable to run anything without getting very puffed up with their own importance. It is a toddler group, for heaven's sake, not an international conference trying to organise world peace, so try to keep things in perspective. The worst scenario is that there will be a crowd of overbearing mothers trying to keep up with the Joneses, trumpeting loudly about their offspring's accomplishments and explaining how they themselves still manage to run their company single-handedly, despite all the pressures of motherhood. Leave. Find another group and enjoy your get-togethers with like-minded women who think parenthood is possibly the best thing that has ever happened to them, but feel that it is also rather nice to have some time to themselves.

If you do become part of a group while your baby is fairly young, you will feel confident about watching your child play with other youngsters and have the pleasure of seeing them all develop together. This also allows for development of the tact and diplomacy needed to cope with these fraught situations where the children start interacting rather more forcefully than you had ever anticipated. There is an unwritten rule that each mother keeps a watchful eye on her own child's behaviour, ready to scold her into next week should she attack some unsuspecting little soul playing nearby. All that should be required of the victim's mother is suitable kissing and cuddling, a gracious acceptance of the other mother's apology and a silent vow never to let your angel near that thug again. It doesn't always work like that, if only because parents have such different views on what is acceptable behaviour. However, it doesn't matter if the aggressor is too young to realise how much pain she is inflicting and also too young to discuss sensibly the implications of her behaviour – if the parent doesn't immediately react and end the assault then feel at liberty to do so yourself, making a heroic effort to ignore any comments such as 'children invariably work out their own disputes'. Possibly, but I am not sure that ten-month-old babies tearing out each other's hair have read the rules on resolving conflicts calmly.

In the end, the only test of how much good these sessions do you – and for the moment we are concentrating on your needs, rather than your child's – is how much you enjoy them. I have made some really good friends and a lot of acquaintances, and have come to the conclusion that it doesn't matter how mature you are, there will always be someone you can hate silently and viciously! It does help to spend time with other people who are at the same stage in life as you, and while there will always be some immaculate, calm and usually excellent mother to make you feel two inches high, there will also be someone who is scruffier, more unfit and covered in more babysick than you could ever have imagined. This is also a good opportunity to watch child-minders and nannies in action, and decide what sort of care you will be opting for when you go back to work. Sometimes you can be very lucky, and discover someone who is excellent at her job but will soon be looking for another child to care for because her current charge is moving on to nursery, or whatever. If you have seen someone in action with small children and like the way she works, you will get a far better idea of her capabilities than in an interview situation. Similarly, if you think 'nightmare nanny!' every time you clap eyes on a particular child-minder, you know exactly what you are not looking for, and will go out of your way to make sure there is no chance of your child being cared for by someone similar.

Remember your Partner

In the middle of all this fitness and self-expression, there is one area which should never be overlooked. By now you will have great confidence in yourself as a parent, and will usually be able to face the day reasonably calmly, having learned to organise yourself around the endless run of chores which come with a baby. Even if you have a disastrous run of events which can so easily coincide and ruin your day, you have been there before and can turn your back on the chaos and concentrate on the important things. And, strangely enough, one of the most important things is the chap who comes rushing home every night to a bit of baby-worship. You are his partner, not his mum, and if you want an equal relationship there are a couple of things you need to do to maintain your original roles. If you have reached the stage of maternity leave which means that you are receiving minimum wages or are unpaid, then it is tempting to slip into humble mode because he is out there struggling to bring home the cash. Assuming that you both agreed on the type of leave you wanted and could afford to take, please remember your original considerations. You are not lounging around at home living the life of Riley; you are also doing a full-time job, which happens to be child-minding. If everything is running so smoothly that you are quite happy to take on all the cleaning, cooking and shopping chores too, then fine, but don't start playing Martyr Mary because of some misplaced guilt complex.

If you do plan to go back to work and you have got yourself firmly established as chief cook and bottle-washer, laundry woman, cleaner and organiser of every other mind-numbing chore imaginable, you are going to have a very hard time getting shot of this image without a distinct threat to marital harmony. It is easy to get used to having someone else do all the dirty work, and if anyone was daft enough to do that for me I would accept like a shot, walk all over him and be well put out if he dared to try and change the status quo. A good compromise is to make sure that he knows how much you can manage to do without feeling put upon or taken for granted, and no matter how saintly your child I would suggest that your partner does at least as much as he would have to if he were living alone. When the time comes for your return to work you will have to make sure you renegotiate terms and conditions before they become a bone of contention. Most of us don't have the luxury of much spare time to waste keeping our living quarters spick and span and have to get by with the bare minimum, which is always easier when the two of you do some sort of sharing.

Most of this is based on the assumption that the mum is the primary carer, which is still usually the case. However, more and more dads are becoming the full-time carer, so I apologise for my sexism in this area. However, irrespective of which parent is at home, remember that your partner is still out there in the big, bad world, and would probably give their eyeteeth to be at home with the baby. Being responsible for providing the main income can be pretty daunting stuff, and a bit of appreciation doesn't go amiss.

As such, if you have had the world's worst day at home, let your partner in the door before you start mouthing off about the trials and tribulations of parenthood. Sometimes you reach breaking point, and the mess of unwashed dishes, dirty clothes and bedlam, compounded by a screaming baby, is just too much. Get rid of the worst. Shove all the clothes in the washing machine, the dishes in the sink and pile everything else into a large plastic bag or cardboard box, to be sorted out at a less hectic moment. Clear all surface junk in this way and everything starts to look just a little better, even you.

Run yourself a deep, warm bath and bring the baby either in with you or just into the bathroom to watch. Lie back and think of nothing, even if the baby is yelling in your ear. You can switch off for ten minutes without doing anything or anybody any harm, and in that time wash your hair, scrub yourself from head to foot, and shed your irritations like an old skin. Wrap yourself up in the biggest towel you own, and dry your hair. The noise of a hairdryer is such a bland sound that it stops some babies from roaring – it is worth a try, but if it doesn't work at least you will feel clean, sweet and freshly groomed. Put on clean clothes from the skin out – nobody said that they have to be ironed – root out a packet of pasta and all your work is done. I am not an advocate of the 'get dressed and made up to greet your husband' brigade, but I am a firm believer in making yourself feel and look better. It is rather pleasant to give up the frumpy image from time to time and refuse to look like something the cat wouldn't drag in, and the knock-on effect is that making yourself look better invariably has you feeling better. Besides, superb mother that you are, you are still an intelligent, articulate, attractive woman first and foremost. If you believe it, then so will everyone else.

Chapter Five

Health and Fitness: Baby's

Shortly after your child arrives you will realise that there is now one major area of contention between you and the rest of the world. Your baby is quite simply perfect, but less discerning people keep using words like 'average' or 'normal'. Accept that they do not have the highly developed skills and perception that you are clearly gifted with, and pretend that your infant is the same as Joe Bloggs's down the road. It makes for an easier life if you keep your child's god-like qualities to yourself, preventing forcing feelings of inferiority on the less fortunate.

To generalise, the average newborn baby is about seven and a half pounds, with colouring usually, though not always, inherited from the parents, and a cry that shocks you into action every time. Having spent nine months curled up, she still shows a fondness for this position for some time and will even appear to be very wary of being picked up carelessly. Depending on her arrival method, her head and skin can indicate any medical help that was given, such as pressure marks from forceps or ventouse delivery, or even a squashed nose or ears from a normal vaginal delivery. Babies born by Caesarean section look very smooth and untouched by comparison, but within a matter of days, or even hours, they all appear as perfect as each other.

Some time after the baby's birth, when she has been cleaned up, cord clamped and has nappy in place, she will be given back to you to unwrap and check that everything is as it should be. It is like the best Christmas present ever, but it is so new that you can't help asking how everything works. You examine the baby from head to foot, and all the information you gathered so carefully over the last nine months goes right out of your head. She might be covered in fine hair, or be very pink, while her hands and feet are often a bluish colour for a short time. Her nails can be remarkably long and sharp, which means that in no time at all she inflicts horrific-looking scratches on her tiny face. A good pair of baby scissors and a pair of scratch mitts is your best bet in these circumstances.

During the first few days you are usually still in hospital, so the staff are always available to answer all your queries, ranging as they do from how to clean what remains of the cord, to wondering why your baby doesn't want to open her eyes. Watching the action couldn't be further removed from what you have read and learned before the event. We are all told that the baby's first bowel movements are referred to as meconium, a sticky, greeny-black substance which can take three days to clear. Sounds reasonable enough. What actually happens is that this stuff resembles nothing more than tar, sticks firmer than superglue, and the average baby not only passes it, but blows it out with such force that it covers clothes and cot as well as nappy.

Once this stage is over, the nappies of breast-fed babies contain a mustard-yellow, inoffensive substance, while bottle-fed babies produce something browner, firmer and smellier. How often they will have a dirty nappy is another poser, because some babies will have a bowel movement practically every time they pass urine, and others will perform once or twice a day. Either is normal, although bottle-fed babies have a tendency to become constipated, a problem which breast-fed babies do not suffer from. The important thing to watch out for is the amount of wet nappies, if you have any fear of dehydration. If you are concerned about too many dry nappies have a word with your nurse or GP.

FEAR OF COT DEATH

A constant worry for parents is the fear of cot death, and it is one which haunts us all. The publicity about preventing this has, quite rightly, made us all very aware of the tragedies which can occur, to the extent that some people become almost obsessed by it. This is a small price to pay if the fatality figures keep coming down and concerned parents keep putting pressure on the government to continue with research. As already mentioned, follow the official guidelines about preventing cot death, especially where smoking is concerned. It doesn't matter if you hurt Granny's feelings by making her puff away in a freezing garden and then forbidding her to kiss her precious grandchild because she will still be oozing nicotine from every pore – she would be a sight more hurt and upset if anything happened to the little mite.

I have always felt better for having the cradle next to my bed for the first year, which is perhaps a little excessive! We are then forced to admit that we reach a point when the baby is actually disturbed by us, and it is time to move her away from our disruption, usually when she is about a year old. Even when you are exhausted you quickly develop a strange sixth sense which has you leaping awake at every little sound from the cot, even something as unromantic as breaking wind. We were given a baby alarm as a gift when our first daughter was born, and it has undoubtedly been one of the most reassuring things I have used over the last five years. I am also a great believer in demand feeding and lifting a tiny baby as soon as she needs reassurance, and the alarm certainly helps a great deal in both these circumstances.

Tiny babies also have a very disconcerting habit of breathing so quietly that you practically have to get into the pram to hear them. This is not a test, a practical joke or an attempt to finish you off through sheer fright, although you might start to suspect that it is all part of some fiendish plot as you hyperventilate for the third time in a week. Practically every parent I know can recount a tale of frantically waking up a peacefully sleeping baby who, not surprisingly, took complete umbrage at such an invasion of their privacy. In my case, the first time my daughter scared the wits out of me with this little party trick was during my attempt at the first proper Sunday dinner since her arrival. Not only did I put my husband (and myself) off our lovingly made strawberry cheesecake, I actually stood on mine when I dropped the plate and tried to insert my entire upper body into the pram. I still hold a grudge for that. One day when she is just a bit bigger she will be forced to cook me a Sunday dinner to make up, and I don't care how long I have to wait for it.

SKIN CONDITIONS

From a serious subject to a much more frivolous one, and one which is likely to cause us grief for most of our lives: skin, and in particular the little faces. Even the most doting parent has to admit that milk rashes, dry skin and cradle cap aren't the most beautifying conditions, but they do clear up fairly quickly. Milk rashes are odd little things, and you never feel that you get a terribly satisfactory explanation for them. They are small, white, pinhead spots running from the bridge of the nose to the cheeks, with the odd one appearing around the eyes. Apparently, your baby's glands are inexperienced in getting rid of impurities, and this is the result. They cause no harm, need no treatment and disappear by themselves, so resist the temptation to go for some home-beauty-salon attacks on this delicate skin. Squeezing, swabbing or over-cleansing will result only in lasting marks, so give them all a miss. Dry skin should be treated with a little more respect, especially if there is a family tendency to eczema. Avoid any strong or scented shampoos, baby bath oils or soaps and check with your pharmacist about any oily preparations which can be usefully added to the bath water. If you do suspect eczema see your GP, as they like to pre-empt possible problems in this area and make sure you are using the right products from the beginning. Cradle cap is another easily treated condition, although it can look perfectly horrid – crusty, yellow-brown scales of skin which can cover most of the head. Massage olive or baby oil into the scalp, leave for a few hours or overnight, and then gently comb out the debris before shampooing. Repeat the process until the rough skin is completely cleared, but check it every so often for a possible recurrence.

NAPPY RASH

Nappy rash is agony for everyone concerned, and sometimes older children are the real sufferers, especially if they have moved on to drinks and solids which make bowel movements and urine much stronger. Baby wipes are very handy, especially when dealing with soiled nappies, but they can dry out the skin and exacerbate any tendency to nappy rash. Try to keep the wipes for occasions when you are out and about, and use warm, soapy water at home. Always make sure the skin is completely dry after washing, and use a good barrier cream like Sudocrem either all the time, or at the first hint of trouble. If you are environmentally friendly and using terry nappies they will need to be changed more frequently than disposables, as they become waterlogged very quickly. The disadvantage with disposables is that they are now so refined, with scientifically researched layers drawing all liquid away from the skin, that it is hard to tell just how wet they are, short of wringing them out.

When nappy rash does strike it can be for a number of reasons, so various treatments must be considered. Initially the condition begins with reddened and obviously uncomfortable skin, and if it is allowed to become more severe the skin cracks, sometimes blistering and bleeding. The constant assault of bacteria in the form of normal nappy contents can lead to a thrush infection, and the problems really begin, as it seems to be well-nigh impossible to heal. The single most constant advice you will get is to wash and dry the suffering bottom, and leave off the nappy, allowing fresh air to do the best healing. There is a limit, however, to how long you can leave a tiny bottom bare to the four winds, especially in wintertime. At night-time it is practically impossible, if only because natural body functions will soon have your baby lying in a cold, wet puddle, or worse. Not surprisingly, this condition distresses even the youngest baby, and before long you find yourself on a treadmill of different treatments, none of which you give a reasonable time to work.

Watching a tiny baby cry as you clean her skin is heart-rending, but before you go down the road of trying every cream and potion now available I would suggest that you try one of the oldest remedies still in use. Firstly, confirm with your doctor whether the baby has thrush, as you will need a particular type of ointment to clear this up. In every other case, no matter how minor or severe, wash the skin with warm, soapy water, rinse and dry gently, but thoroughly. A hairdryer on gentle heat is ideal for this and, after their initial surprise, babies find it soothing and comforting. Now comes the cold bit, which they don't like at first. Dip cotton wool into the white of an egg, and pat gently all over the affected area, again drying with a hairdryer. They protest at first, but again the warmth will calm them down. The egg white dries to a shiny, impenetrable skin, able to withstand the most noxious nappy contents. If you want to make absolutely sure, repeat the process two to three times, drying thoroughly between layers.

Apparently this remedy has been in use for generations, and it is easily the most effective. Doing this even for a day keeps the irritants away from the painful skin, and gives it a chance to heal. Once the inflammation has started to die down, use this treatment at every other nappy change, alternating with the same cleaning process and a big dollop of Sudocrem, rather than egg white. Over the next few days, gradually reduce the use of the egg white, but make sure that any ulcerated or bleeding areas are well protected. If you have been given a thrush treatment you will often find that this is sufficient on its own, but if not use the egg white system until there is some sign of recovery, then return to the prescribed treatment. This method can be used at the first hint of nappy rash, thus preventing any nasty outbreaks, and is also extremely useful for older toddlers with upset stomachs or diarrhoea which in turn breaks down delicate skin. An appropriate painkiller can also help the little sufferer, but please check with your GP as to what is suitable for young babies.

Thrush doesn't just appear in the nappy area, but is actually more common orally. It looks like small white milk patches on the tongue and the inside of the cheeks, but if you touch the patches gently with a clean fingernail they won't come off, unlike milk curds. The treatment is usually anti-candida drops, which clear the problem very quickly. If you find that your nipples are sore at the same time, you and your baby could be simply passing the infection to and from each other, so make sure you get the appropriate treatment to stop any recurrence.

Babies are experts at throwing up, and seem to have a marked preference for your smartest clothes as target practice. In a large crowd of beautifully dressed businessmen and women you can easily spot the relatively new parents. Either they have strange little white stains around about their shoulders, or the same shoulders are very obviously recently sponged. A pack of muslin nappies is the soundest investment you can make for this condition, tossed over your shoulders, mopping up all the different areas your infant will reach and making the constant changing of baby clothes and bedding unnecessary.

There is a condition called projectile vomiting which can indicate a need for treatment, as the child doesn't retain food long enough to get any benefit from it, but this is a very noticeable illness and could never be confused with the normal spits and sickness of the average baby. Anyone whose baby suffers from this is likely to have reached their GP long before I or anyone else urges them to do so, as it is difficult to ignore it when your baby is doing a vomiting exercise which rivals the worst scenes in *The Exorcist*! With most children, you just have to put up with it until they grow out of it, and make sure that a plentiful supply of bibs stops them looking, feeling or smelling too sticky or offensive. This is another of these infant side effects which disappear literally overnight, but no one can give an estimated date for desisting.

Upset Tummies and Other Minor Ailments

Upset tummies are more likely in older children, and vomiting should be treated by giving sips of clear liquid, such as water or diluted lemonade. There are preparations you can get from the chemist which are meant to replace all the essential sugars and chemicals a child loses when vomiting, but they normally taste pretty foul. It is bad enough feeling sick without being forced to drink some nauseating concoction! Stick to the diluted lemonade in small amounts, and you won't go far wrong. The aim is to get any infection out of the digestive system, and reducing intake to clear fluids will obviously give this the best chance of occurring. As with all illness, if your instinct tells you that this is more serious than a quick bout of throwing up, contact your GP for help.

Eye problems are common and usually minor, such as 'sticky eye', where there is some ongoing irritation which can look like an infection. This usually comes to nothing, and bathing the eyes with cooled, boiled water is the recommended way to clear it. Blocked tear ducts can leave your baby damp-eyed and tragic in appearance, as the tears ooze down the little cheeks on every occasion. You will be shown how to use gentle massage to help clear the blockage and, as in cases of sticky eye, the area must be kept clean to avoid infection. The tear ducts will normally clear within six months, but the rare cases which don't can be surgically corrected at a later date by a very simple procedure.

Your baby's belly button will initially look raw and painful as the remainder of the cord dries up and falls off. Like so many other things connected with tiny babies this is most certainly not the case unless infection sets in, and again you will be shown how to care for it and avoid such a possibility.

BIRTHMARKS

Birthmarks are a bit of a misnomer if only because so many of them arrive some time after the baby does. They can also be the source of quite astounding ignorance in the medical profession. I suspect this is because the treatment of birthmarks is such a highly developed science that only the specialists could possibly be abreast of the latest developments. This won't, however, stop some misguided health visitors saying 'she will just have to learn to live with it, and you can get some great cover make-up now'. You certainly can, but that is not the point. Babies do not automatically arrive blemish-free, as I pointed out earlier, but most of these marks, such as the red 'stork bites' or the bruise-like 'Mongolian blue spots', fade away in their own time. The views of the past, where some marks were considered permanent and disfiguring, no longer hold good. Modern techniques in the treatment of birthmarks and blemishes have improved dramatically, and continue to develop, almost overnight.

True birthmarks are areas of discoloured skin caused by abnormal blood vessels or pigmentation, and tend to be classed in two different groups, determined by their colour. Red birthmarks come in two main types: strawberry marks and port wine stains. They result from the baby having too many tiny blood vessels in a particular area of skin, and the medical term for both these conditions is haemangioma. Strawberry marks are sometimes referred to as strawberry naevus, and are lumpy, raised, red swellings. They can grow very quickly but the vast majority don't need treatment and disappear naturally. Approximately half have gone by the time the child is five, and 90 per cent by the age of nine.

Laser treatment reduces redness, and plastic surgery can be offered to remove any loose skin left by the mark or to tidy up the area where the birthmark was. Port wine stains are usually much larger, flat, purple-red marks which can appear anywhere, but often affect the face and neck. They don't fade with time, and will grow with the child unless treated. Previously there was a risk of scarring with laser treatment, but children as young as six weeks can now be safely and successfully treated. A short general anaesthetic is necessary for small children as the patient must be completely still, but older children and adults may need only a local anaesthetic to numb the affected area, which can sting slightly during treatment.

The laser works by directing a concentrated beam of light at the extra blood vessels or pigment cells to destroy them. Around eight or nine treatments, usually every couple of months, are needed to treat a typical port wine stain, and the results have been very encouraging, with the mark either clearing completely or lightening considerably. Brown birthmarks include moles, freckles and *café au lait* spots and are caused by an over-activity of the skin cells that produce melanin, the pigment that promotes a tan when exposed to the sun. Brown birthmarks tend to be more difficult to treat, but medical advances in lasers are getting some promising results. *Café au lait* spots are pale, coffee-coloured, oval patches which appear anywhere on the body and can range in size. They can be hardly noticeable, but laser treatment can sometimes lighten darker or more prominent areas.

Although the initial reaction to a birthmark might be panic, it is worth while considering the options. In the first instance, parents should contact their GP and ask to be referred to a specialist. If you don't feel entirely confident that you are being given the most up-to-date information, the Disfigurement Guidance Centre in Fife are extremely well informed. They also have a book which parents can use to raise the issue of treatment with their children, called *Puss Puss and the Magic Laser*. The important thing is to feel that you know exactly what is on offer regarding different treatments and their results. In some cases, lasers are developing so rapidly that it is worth waiting as long as possible for maximum success. Children can be very relaxed about birthmarks if parents can give them the confidence to deal with any questions from their peers. Calling the mark a 'beauty spot' can be enough to deflect any possible teasing, and an awareness that it will be treated in the future can transform the effect it will have on the child. Pigmentation marks in particular should be protected by total sunblock in sunny weather to prevent darkening. This is available on prescription, as is concealing make-up, and if you are unsure about any aspect of your child's treatment, go back to the specialist. More than anyone, he or she will be aware of how bright the outlook now is for children with birthmarks, and how sophisticated the treatment is becoming.

PROTECTION IN THE SUN
Going back to the subject of sun, it is far too easy to forget

how delicate baby skin is. On a scorching day, or even the mild warmth which passes for summer in this country, it is very tempting to leave your baby sleeping or relaxing in direct sunshine. Don't even think about it! You might think that tanning yourself to the colour and texture of old boots is still a sophisticated thing to do, but you couldn't be further from the truth. The emphasis for everyone, but especially for children, should be on covering up. Right from the baby's birth, get into the habit of using total sunblocks, sunhats and T-shirts and shady parasols or umbrellas. Never leave a baby unattended in a hot car, and if you have to travel any distance make sure the child is as cool as possible and out of direct sunlight. You can also get a variety of blinds to use in the car which help to keep your baby as safe as possible.

Once children become mobile it is harder to take all the necessary precautions to prevent sunburn, and rubbing cream all over a wriggling and slippery toddler can be a nightmare. On warm days it is as easy to make sunblock part of the routine. When you are getting them dressed, and before the nappy goes on, cover them with cream from head to toe. Make it a game, get them to help or offer a reward, until it becomes so much part of the routine that complaints are desultory and ignored. You can also buy total sunblock in sticks of startling colours which make it less of a chore and more of a fun face-painting effort. Topping up the cream throughout the day is always easier, especially if you feel that you managed to get a good, thick layer on first thing.

Insist on a hat which covers the neck and a loose T-shirt to protect shoulders and little arms, and simply refuse to let them out without it. Even those with the strongest nudist tendencies give in to such brutal tactics when threatened with being stuck indoors on lovely days. They can still run naked from time to time, but if you make sure that it is in the late afternoon rather than the heat of the day they will have the same fun with none of the lingering afterburn. Children adore messing around in paddling pools, buckets of water and at the seaside, but that will invariably wash off some of your extensive protection. Reapply regularly, trying not to rub in sand along with the cream! If all fails, and someone gets a bit too much sun, treat the affected parts with calamine cream (which is less drying than calamine lotion), or apply natural yoghurt to take the heat out of the skin. In all cases, keep the child well out of the sun until the affected area has recovered and avoid overwarm baths, as this can be agonising on hot, tight skin. Some children can be very badly affected by excess sun, and may feel sick and dizzy. Let them lie down, preferably in a darkened room, with occasional sips of water until the dizziness has passed. If they are affected once in this way it is likely to recur, so make sure they follow all the rules about care in the sun.

COLDS, HIGH TEMPERATURES AND INFECTIONS

In all probability the first illness your baby will suffer from will be the common cold, but your reaction will be one of total panic, instead of taking it all in your stride. This is not the best time to tell you, but some statistics claim that the average child will have nine colds a year until well after they start school! You won't be able to avoid all the germs being shared in toddler groups, nursery and then school, but it does seem a bit harsh when a weeks-old baby starts snuffling and spluttering.

I haven't tried the next piece of folklore, although I know several mothers who swear by it. At the first sign of a runny nose, they recommend squirting a few drops of breast milk up each nostril. Do it as if you were hand-expressing, and apparently the milk comes out in a spray which is fine enough not to have the baby sneezing it straight back at you. It is probably worth a try, as it certainly can't do the baby any harm

– unless you pour pints of the stuff up her nose! – and breast milk is said to have healing properties which even the finest medical research hasn't yet discovered.

This method apart, the only treatment is no treatment at all, and the cold will clear up in about seven days. The most troublesome aspect for a small baby is that it hampers her feeding considerably, as it is obviously very difficult to breathe and suck at the same time. Don't try to clear babies' noses with cotton buds or rolled-up tissues as this is interference they can well do without, although wiping runny noses is always a good idea. Some babies get very upset when they are snuffly, from a mixture of frustration, discomfort and straightforward annoyance at having to work so hard for a decent feed, but lots of cuddles and attention go a long way towards solving that problem.

Propping the head of the cot up slightly can help breathing at night, and there are various decongestants available which you sprinkle on bedding, but doctors recommend them only for babies over three months. A little Baby Vick can be used at any age, as it is very mild and might be just enough to help unblock those little passages. Tempting though it is to tuck children up warmly, try not to let them get too hot as fevers and high temperatures bring their own problems. Babies have a bit of a problem with controlling their own thermostat, and if their temperature gets too high there is a very real danger of febrile convulsions. This is rare, but utterly terrifying if it happens to you. Don't shock or frighten babies with icy baths or freezing fans, but sponge them down with tepid water until they start to cool. You don't have to be brave here, but it helps to remain as calm as possible. Phone your doctor or local hospital (ask for Casualty) for help, but treat your child as you wait for their assistance. Follow any advice they give you, which will probably be the above measures to get their temperature down. Paracetamol such as Calpol helps to lower temperatures, but again this is a drug given to young babies only on the advice of a doctor.

Fortunately, this condition is extremely rare in very young babies, and the only reason I am mentioning it and scaring you into fits yourself is the principle that forewarned is forearmed. If your child suffers from a febrile convulsion once, this apparently makes it more likely that it will happen again, and you will be given very clear advice from your doctor or hospital both on how to prevent it and on how to treat it if it does occur.

Another little extra which comes with colds is ear infections, and medical opinion is fairly evenly divided on how to treat them. One elderly lady of my acquaintance likes to point out loudly that sore ears were very common in her day, claiming: 'there was none of this nonsense about it. We just went to bed with our heads on a hot water bottle until the ear drum burst and the pus ran out.' Well, it sounds straightforward, if rather painful, but she doesn't like to be reminded that it happened so often that everyone in her family of seven is deaf to some extent. Maybe that is why she is so loud about it! The other extreme is constant antibiotics, and the automatic insertion of grommets to allow the infection to drain. Nowadays, doctors are understandably cautious about prescribing antibiotics at the drop of a hat, having no desire to see children grow up immune to some of the most precious drugs available to us. However, ear infections can be excruciatingly painful, and although the eardrum can burst and heal over a number of times without lasting damage, the medical profession are reluctant to let this happen too often. As such, although they will let minor chest infections and green noses take their own good time to clear, ear infections are more likely to warrant a mild course of antibiotics, along with Calpol to ease the pain. The good news is that most children grow out of ear infections, as all their passages grow with them and are less likely to harbour large amounts of mucus which is ready and waiting to become infected.

There is another option which is becoming more and more popular, and that is homeopathy. This is one of these things which provokes extreme reactions: either you swear by it, or you consider it to be nothing more than hocus-pocus. Just to be different, I can't decide what I think, having taken my daughters to a homeopath when they were four and one respectively to have treatment for the dreaded ear infections. In the event, they were given both prophylactic treatment and medicine for a current infection, and the elder has rarely been troubled with ear problems since, although there hasn't been much of a positive response from the younger one. What I don't know is whether the four-year-old was at the perfect age just to grow out of ear infections, and I doubt whether anyone could tell me for sure. Remember that you will usually have to pay for homeopathic consultations, and they don't come particularly cheap. Another area where this form of treatment is becoming popular is for allergic reactions, although this would normally be only for skin complaints and not for the violent physical reactions which can result from things like peanuts or bee stings.

MENINGITIS

Parents by nature are terrific worriers, and very often the object of our concern does not deserve the attention we give it. However, when it comes to illness there is one in particular which we all dread, yet it is one which deserves every moment we concentrate on it. Meningitis strikes terror into the heart of every parent, and if you are ever concerned about your child's symptoms in this respect, do not hesitate to contact your doctor immediately. I knew very little about meningitis before my children were born, and in many respects I'm still very ignorant, but our GPs have made sure that we feel confident about calling them out.

If your child is clearly ill and disinterested in everything around her, or is excessively sleepy, disturbed by bright lights, or appears to have a stiff or painful neck or a pin-prick rash, get help immediately. Most doctors are perfectly happy to be called out to check a potentially dangerous situation. For the first year after I became a mum I seemed to spend a lot of my time pathetically apologising to our doctors for dragging them out at all hours of the day, night and weekend, but every time I was confronted with a situation which left me uneasy I was too scared not to. Maybe they wanted to shriek at me to stop being such an over-reacting, paranoid, first-time mother, but they hid it well, even in the middle of the night. On one particular occasion, my call-out had been the doctor's sixth of the night and it was still only 4 a.m., but he still managed to reassure me that it is better to be safe. You can't be too careful with babies and small children.

MAINTAINING A GOOD RELATIONSHIP WITH YOUR DOCTOR
Children are very good at lying obviously ill in your arms right up to the moment your doctor walks in the door, only to transform instantly into a vibrant picture of health. Good doctors understand this. They know that they have been highly trained to assess just such conditions, while the rest of us function on blind parental panic. However, striking a balance between good medical care and taking advantage of an excellent medical practice is a compromise both parties must enter into. If you don't feel totally at ease with the care provided then shop around a bit, but try to be fair. Most of us expect the world and its doctors to revolve around our offspring, but this in itself is a reasonably short-lived condition and we can be persuaded to settle down and stop treating everything as a dire emergency.

By their very nature, childhood illnesses can appear to be emergencies, if only because the little darlings can change so rapidly and make their pain known so loudly. I have lost count of the number of times a cold has become a vicious ear infection in the space of two hours and always outwith normal surgery time so that I end up whining down the phone for an emergency appointment. There have been times when I am convinced that our surgery staff must think our family incapable of being ill, or at least noticing we're unwell, during the course of the usual working day. However, it has to be said that the doctors all have families of their own and must be used to grovelling parents, because they are very good at reassuring us that children don't fit in with carefully organised plans and times.

Before we started a family we had been perfectly happy with our doctors, but it was then surprising to find out how many of our friends who already had children had either moved to the practice on the advice of other parents, or like us were already part of it simply by good chance and found it met all their needs. What I also found very interesting was the response from other medical experts, such as the community midwives, when they asked what practice we were with. Invariably their reaction was extremely positive, and we kept being told what an excellent reputation our doctors had, particularly when it came to childcare.

The practice is very popular and very busy, but all the staff manage to retain a personal touch. If I phone for an appointment and the next available is 24 hours away, I am asked whether this is suitable or if the matter is urgent. This gives me a reasonable chance to act like a responsible adult, and confirm that a bout of sinusitis is not life-threatening. However, should you have a genuine concern and feel that you cannot wait, you will always be given the chance to speak to a doctor about the symptoms. If he or she agrees that it is unwise to leave a nasty case of mastitis or an infection for another night, you are always fitted in for an emergency appointment. It is a courteous, effective and non-patronising system which works beautifully, and would make an ideal blueprint for any medical practitioners who believe they are too important to consider the patients as individuals.

Coming to terms with the realisation that you are responsible for your baby is hard enough in normal circumstances, but illness can undermine the most confident parent. In time you will undoubtedly learn what constitutes a major problem and what simply sounds or looks rather awful. Remember as well that there is excellent medical backup to the service provided by your GP in the shape of your practice nurse or local pharmacist. However, have confidence in your own instincts, and if illness or diagnosis leaves you unhappy, tell your doctor your fears. Doctors are not mind-readers, and the best of them will agree that parental instinct can sometimes pick up on something missed by everyone else. This has saved lives; we have all heard stories of parents who refused to accept what appeared to be a correct diagnosis and insisted on further investigation which revealed something much more serious. Be firm but polite and don't start shouting the odds, because nobody responds well in that situation. Hopefully, however, you will never find yourself in such a stressful situation and the worst thing you will ever have to contend with is a bad cold.

There may be situations when your child will have to be hospitalised, but in the main this only becomes traumatic for older children if they are ill-prepared for this eventuality. If a young baby has to be kept in for any reason, then mum at least, and possibly dad, should be able to stay in with them. This normally also applies to older children, although you may find yourself with only a chair to sleep in and no hope of even a camp bed. It is uncomfortable and it can be frustrating, but if your child is happier, that is all that matters. If your child is admitted to hospital suddenly you will have no time to prepare her, so reassurance and a positive attitude are vital from the start. It is hard to hide panic, but try to do so, if only to calm her. Children are very quick to sense agitation in adults, so this can be a real exercise in control to stop them from becoming anxious.

If you know in advance that she is being admitted for some reason you will have plenty of time to prepare her, and often the hospital staff will provide helpful hints and literature to make everything go smoothly. Talk about what is going to happen, and even try to make it into an adventure. Depending on the age of the child, bribery and corruption are very useful tools, and a shiny new doctor's set could be just what is needed! It is often not easy to keep to your usual routine, but if Mum and Dad are the same as ever, the child will be more relaxed. Don't scare her by suddenly giving in to all her demands; one bright little six-year-old who was having a very simple ear operation said, 'I thought I was dying because Mum and Dad gave me everything I asked for and no rows when I was bad.' You can understand her reasoning, as her parents' caring efforts had totally backfired and left her petrified rather than reassured.

From Wind to Teeth

Most of the time your baby's ailments will be minor or merely an intrinsic part of her development. One of the first things we all do with a new baby is 'get her wind up', and everyone has a favoured method: over your knee, on the shoulder, or perhaps with the baby upright on your lap, but bent neatly in the middle. Lots of babies don't need very much in the way of help when it comes to expelling wind from either end, while other poor souls make a real song and dance about it after every feed, with their knees drawn up in pain and shrieks of anguish at the air rattling round inside them. This solves itself with time, as their systems become mature enough to cope, but how you deal with it at its worst is really up to the individual. Soothing rocking and rubbing can almost hypnotise a baby enough so that they relax and let it all out, while carrying them upright in a sling against your body is an old but trusted remedy.

There are various gripe waters and other concoctions on the market, but most of these aren't recommended for children under three months. Back to Granny, and the old wives' tales, and this is the one that has my personal vote of confidence. Feed the baby sips of cooled, boiled water from a teaspoon, and rub her back firmly. I don't know how it works, but it has always been successful with my lot, to the extent that it sometimes sounded like a controlled explosion. The powers of expulsion from tiny babies never ceases to amaze me, especially when they manage to cover all their clothing from the skin out! Nobody ever thinks to warn you that in one day alone, a week-old baby could require half a dozen changes of clothing. That is a lot of hand-washing, and a chance to discover just how dedicated a mother you really are. Usually, it is also around this time that you realise what a versatile piece of equipment you have in the average washing machine.

Teething is another little gem, where you don't know where you are from one moment to the next, and neither does your poor baby. To be fair, there are a few whose pearly whites appear as painlessly as stars at night, but most are heralded by gnawing, dribbling, shiny red cheeks and general tetchiness, which is understandable when you see the red, swollen gums and the sheer length of time it takes for some to get through. Babies can start teething as early as four months or as late as a year, and even within a family there will be no set pattern. The best time to discover new teeth is not when your baby takes a sharp bite out of your nipple – this can only be described as utter anguish. Whatever you do, do not leap back in horror, as the chances are that she will simply dig the molar in and you will find yourself suffering from rubber nipple syndrome, where the darn thing is elongated by an inch or so. Stay calm, say 'No!' very loudly and firmly (if you can still speak through your tears), and ease your little finger into the side of your baby's mouth to break the suction. The theory behind this is good, and the immediate reaction of taking the child away from the beloved breast works extremely well in most cases, but until she learns that if she bites she doesn't get a drink from you, every time you go to feed reduces you to a shuddering wreck.

I'm sorry, but having had a biter who defied my local NCT by proving that it is possible to suck and bite at the same time, all I can do is sympathise, rather than come up with alternative solutions. Babies all give up nibbling in time, but whether they have become bottle-fed by then probably depends very much on your pain threshold. This is not the time to leave them suffering in silence, either. Painful gums can reduce the happiest children to a miserable wreck, so dish out something to take the edge off their suffering, whether it is the ever-useful Calpol, old-fashioned homeopathic powders or teething gel. Many doctors say that teething does not upset a child's tummy, but lots of others disagree, saying that the over-production of saliva can have a knock-on and nasty effect on the digestive system. My main advice would be to watch out for nasty nappies leading to equally nasty nappy rash, aiming to pre-empt any problems in this area.

Promoting Good Sleeping Habits

And now we come to something which could never be described as an illness, but can turn the calmest parent into a run-down and nervous wreck: poor sleeping habits. It doesn't help the children either, but they seem better able to cope when they have had a disturbed night than we do. This could be something to do with toddlers' ability to just nod off in their buggies, which is a luxury denied to their long-suffering parents. During the first three months most of us with any grasp on reality expect to be up once or twice in the night to provide nourishment and the odd nappy change. By around three months the real darlings are starting to sleep through the night, and by six months it is not unreasonable to expect all of them to have learned this particular skill. Some do, some don't, some will for a while and then regress horribly. What do you do?

In the first instance, if you are quite happy offering room service in the small hours, then by all means carry on. Just bear in mind that babies who are six months old do not need a night-time feed, and if you are dishing it out now, the chances are that your child will still expect it at ages one, two or even when she has started school. If you are happy with that, then read no further. However, I need my sleep and I am assuming that most of you do too.

The first few months with a new baby are magical, and I am sure you move into an extra gear where you are not only able to cope with the night-time pit-stops, but you actually enjoy them. I love the feeling of being alone with my baby in that peculiar night-time silence, where all that matters is making sure that I am providing everything she needs. Research has shown that babies who are lifted as soon as they cry do not become more demanding as they grow up, but rather less, having had all the reassurance necessary at a very young age. You can get to the point with a tiny baby where her snuffles as she starts to stir are enough to waken you, so night-time becomes even more peaceful without any hungry cries. If things continue to go well, your baby will start to sleep for longer and longer periods, secure in the knowledge that you will always be there if she needs you. Eventually, the last feed at night will be enough to see her comfortably through until the morning, and peace reigns in the household again.

That's the theory, anyway. I really thought we had cracked it with our first daughter. She started sleeping through the night at four months, and we had five months of unbroken nights until she started crying in the middle of the night for no good reason. We ruled out illness and discomfort, and tried walking the floor with her in a vain effort to settle her. Finally, I gave in and offered her a breast feed and that did the trick.

This became a nightly occurrence, and I gave in for the sake of grabbing a few hours' sleep, until she started waking a second time in the night. So there she was at nearly ten months of age, eating for Scotland during the day and then wakening at one and five in the morning for a satisfying drink. She was in terrific shape, and we looked and felt dreadful. We started to suspect that we were approaching the problem in the wrong way when she decided to waken in the evenings, round about ten or eleven, for another little drink. Lack of sleep leaves me totally debilitated, and attempting to sit sensibly at a desk and produce something recognisable as work is well-nigh impossible in those circumstances. Fortunately, the cavalry came to the rescue in the shape of Granny, who firmly believes that being ruled by a ten-month-old baby is not the best way to organise your life. Dr Christopher Green, author of the famous *Toddler Taming*, is also a firm advocate of the following method, so thanks to them both we got ourselves sorted out.

The system is called 'controlled crying', and its main strength lies in being consistent. First of all, establish a good bedtime routine where everyone has a chance to wind down, such as a bath followed by a drink and a cuddle, with a book to induce a little sleepiness. Never use the child's cot, or going to bed, as a punishment, but try to make the room as inviting as possible. Encourage a favourite sleepy-time toy, even if it turns out to be something as unattractive as a hard plastic bucket, or dirty old doll. Go through the same ritual every night and try not to make it too complicated, because if you then try to miss out any of the steps you will be in big trouble! Give big hugs and kisses, and put the child into the cot awake. It is important that children learn to get themselves off to sleep, so that when they waken at night they will be able to drop off again without requiring assistance.

Now for the hard bit – and it is hard, no matter how determined you are. Accept that the next week is going to be a complete wash-out for all involved, and that you will probably be an emotional, self-hating wreck by the end of it. However, the rewards for this steadfast course of action should be everything you want regarding the transformation of your household's sleeping habits. Stay calm, and work on the principle that this is for everyone's benefit. I have to admit that in our house it was Granny who put controlled crying into action, having first banished my husband and me in case we started uncontrolled crying. If you have someone willing to help you with it the first time it is a good idea, if only because it should prevent you and your partner grabbing each other by the throat when you are both desperately looking for someone to pick on!

So, the baby goes to bed and hopefully to sleep, after a gentle winding-down session. Peace reigns for a while, and then the first demanding shrieks are heard. Don't leap immediately into action. Let your baby cry for five minutes, or even longer if you can all stand it, and then go in and soothe her, preferably without lifting, and definitely without offering food or drink. Night-time is for sleeping, not snacking. Once the sniffles have died down, say 'goodnight' and leave. Your baby might be so stunned at your cheek in leaving that crying is forgotten for a while, but that won't last for long, and the screaming will soon start again in earnest. This time, wait for a slightly longer period of time than previously before going back in. Repeat the same procedure, then leave. Again, when the crying resumes, extend the length of time before you return. It sounds simple, but it isn't, if only because you are programmed to leap into action when your child cries. The hardest part is staying consistent, but if you make the mistake of giving in at any time you will have to start from scratch, because your baby now believes that if she cries long enough, you will return and obey orders.

Depending on their age, babies can introduce some fine variations just to keep you on the hop, and filling their nappy is top of the list. Make no particular fuss about this, and give no excessive cuddles or comforting. Just lift, change and return to bed. The famous Granny maintains that you have to have a quiet chat with them to convince them that this is the way things are going to be, and to reassure them that you will always be there if they really need you. I can't quite make up my mind if it is just the effect of soothing tones in the midst of bedlam, but her methods have always worked with her many grandchildren, and you can practically see the baby nodding in agreement as she murmurs 'Time to sleep now . . . no more shouting . . . shut your sleepy eyes . . .'

Seeing their children scream until they throw up is guaranteed to reduce the steeliest parent to floods of apologetic tears – but just stop right there and ask yourself if you want to be vomit-controlled for the next five years before you start grovelling. Again, lift, calm, change – and change the cot if necessary – and return baby to original position with some quiet chat and a firm 'goodnight'. Don't get upset or angry, because reaction is the answer to her prayers. You want her to think that being awake at night is boring – no food, drinks, cuddles or attention – and that you will always come through eventually, but what's the point? Give yourselves a week, trying not to get divorced in the process. In many cases it works in a much shorter time.

One strange side-effect to sorting out night-time sleeping habits is that daytime naps also fall into place, apparently working on the theory that the more you sleep, the more you want to. There will always be times such as during holidays or sickness when your routines and the baby's sleeping patterns will fall by the wayside, but once you have established a reasonable pattern it only takes a short time to get back into the swing of it.

Critics of this method maintain that it doesn't work with everyone and that it is cruel and leaves your child mistrusting you. As I have said before, if having an insomniac wanderer in your house doesn't bother you then don't bother doing anything about it. However, I am not capable of good parenting when I am permanently completely exhausted, and I am very aware of this when I see others in the same situation. I recently took my children to a soft play area for a bit of a rough-and-tumble exercise, and found another mum and her small boy already there and at loggerheads. She was white-faced and shattered, ordering him to 'go and play and enjoy yourself', and he was whining and weepy. Eventually, he took himself off to cry in a corner, and she fell asleep in her chair. Ten minutes later she woke in a panic, to find him still snivelling miserably in the middle of the toys.

By this time she was close to tears herself, and she told me that she hadn't had a complete night's sleep since he was born two years ago. Both of them were suffering terribly from tiredness, as was her husband. The saddest thing of all was that none of the family were enjoying any part of their lives together, and they were locked in a vicious circle. I suggested trying the controlled crying method and she agreed that nothing could be worse than their current situation, but I haven't seen her since so don't know if she tried it. To me, she was the perfect example of how poor sleeping habits can ruin family life, and I consider that a lot more cruel than a week of misery which ends up by rectifying the problem. If you are concerned about your child not trusting you, consider how much more damaging it is to have a bad-tempered, unpredictable parent rather than one who will always appear at times of need, but won't be manipulated. Try it. If you are beyond yourself with lack of sleep, give it a week, then call me everything under the sun if you are convinced you have done it properly and it still doesn't work. However, I would be willing to put money on it that if you stick with it you will be successful – and I promise to resist the temptation to say 'I told you so!'

So here you are, a few months down the line, slim, fit and gorgeous, confident in your parenting abilities and with a perfect child doing everything she is told. Everything is as it should be, so perhaps this is the time to think about picking up your career where you left off. Dream on. Where did you get the idea that anything was going to be that simple ever again?

Chapter Six

Childcare Options

Think work, think childcare, think GUILT. It doesn't matter what situation you are in, you will feel guilty about it at some time or other. This isn't helped by certain right-wing government figures and every Tom, Dick and Harriet feeling it is their God-given right to spout forth about working mothers damaging the youth of today. Let's get a couple of things clear here. There are many parents – male and female – who would be delighted to stay at home and look after their children if they could afford it, if they could take some form of sabbatical without losing their job or damaging their career prospects and if there was a half-decent system of maternity/paternity leave in operation.

However, if you should prefer to carry on with your career while someone else cares for your child, then why the criticism? If a man gives up work solely to be with his child then there is an underlying assumption that he is sponging off the state and not coming up with the goods in providing for his family. Not only that, he is failing to provide a strong role model for his children at the same time as having them suffer financially. However, a woman who does this is popularly seen as a 'good mother', irrespective of the fact that her giving up work can plunge the family into penury. Never mind a strong role model in this instance, all that is needed is a mother who is there all the time, even if this means that she is permanently worried sick about saving pennies and keeping the family out of debt. It is not much good having your mum there all the time if you all end up homeless, so let's go for a sensible balance!

It is tiring having to justify your principles all the time, so don't get into discussions with anyone who is ready to criticise you, especially in the early days when you're not feeling too hot about it all yourself. Try and remember that irrespective of the choice you make, the world is full of harpies ready to point an accusing finger. Their reasoning invariably works as follows. If you work full-time you are a cynical, hard-hearted witch abandoning your offspring for filthy lucre. If you don't work at all you are a shiftless creature who deprives your children of money and the opportunity to look up to a successful parent. And if, like me, you work from home, or part-time, then you fulfil neither role satisfactorily. This is a no-win situation, so don't be drawn. If necessary, be icily polite and suggest that your business is your own.

As I come from and was lucky enough to have then married into the sort of family who believe in letting you make your own decisions, especially when you are obviously an adult, it stuns me when manipulative in-laws appear to have such an effect in some families. I worked with a girl whose baby was cared for by her mum-in-law, and although she may not have paid her in cash for her services, she certainly paid in kind. The family opinion was that she was very lucky to be allowed to work at all, irrespective of the fact that they needed her wages to pay the mortgage. It was conveniently ignored that her salary was the same as her husband's, and instead there was the implication that she should be allowed to carry on with her little job, so long as it didn't interfere with her other duties as wife and mother. Of course, 'other duties' meant all the household chores, including making her husband's packed lunch for him and running his bath every morning so they wouldn't be late leaving for work. We all thought she was completely off her rocker, but nothing anyone said made any difference.

112

After nearly six months of this she cracked in the most impressive way, when her mum-in-law made just one snide comment too many. They had come home from work together, and she asked her husband to peel the potatoes while she changed the baby's nappy. The mum-in-law's reaction was: 'Oh dear, couldn't you try to peel the potatoes the night before? Poor Fred could do with putting his feet up after a hard day's work.' It was the end of civilisation as they knew it. Within ten minutes Fred's mother was in the street with her coat on, Fred was peeling potatoes and grilling chops as if his life depended on it – which it probably did – and they were minus a child-minder and granny in one fell swoop. Strangely enough, Fred had thought his wife liked her life the way it was, reasoning – as men do – that if she had wanted changes she would have mentioned them. Meanwhile he had just gone with the flow, but the resulting explosion left no one in any doubt about fair shares when it came to the dirty work.

STAY IN CHARGE

Good grandparents are worth their weight in gold, but bad ones are everyone's worst nightmare. It is easy for me to say 'don't be pushed around' when I am not in that situation, but having canvassed the opinion of friends who undoubtedly are, their advice is always the same. Think ahead about the precedents you might be setting, and don't fall in with anything just because it has always been the family tradition. Sometimes it is easy to give in for the sake of peace, but it isn't necessarily the wisest solution.

Treat overbearing parents and in-laws in the same way. You are now a parent yourself, and you will make your own decisions. Acknowledge, if you have to, the fact that this probably means that at times you will make your own mistakes, but so what? Stay firm, try not to let resentments build up, and develop a nice line in saying brightly and cheerfully, 'Interesting idea, but not quite what I had in mind', before going your own sweet way. 'Thanks for the suggestion; I'll let you know what we decide', is another good one to avoid being forced into an awkward position, and don't be browbeaten or blackmailed emotionally. We all know families who spend Christmas in abject misery trailing about the countryside to meet the incredible demands of immovable relatives, in some cases in response to the 'never mind me, I'll be all right on my own' type of blackmail. The correct response to this is a cheerful 'Oh, will you? That's fine then', and a fast move on to other subjects. Treat recalcitrant relatives as you would treat equally annoying children, and you won't go far wrong.

On the subject of discipline, this is one area you will need to make your mind up about before committing your child to someone else's care. I don't know about the rest of the world, but I had planned to be a caring, sharing type of mother, the sort who discusses rather than shouts, and who understands youthful frustrations and tantrums rather than being deliberately obstructive. What a great theory, and what a shocking reality. When I was a student, I used to supplement my grant by baby-sitting for my philosophy lecturer, and his children were the sort that made you think sterilisation was no bad thing, even at the tender age of 19.

He and his wife believed in self-expression, in taking out their frustrations on the wooden floor with a mallet rather than chiding the brats, and in empathising with their children about the innate frustrations of being young and powerless. Young and powerless nothing – these mites were about as vulnerable as Attila the Hun on a bad day, and I went off them for good the day they attempted to remove stitches from a wound their cat had suffered. I never did find out how the wound had come about. I went off the self-expressing parents on the day the chap downstairs came up to complain about the noise of the mallet on the wooden floor. He was about six foot square and a bit peeved, and the empathising lecturer took one look at him and lied through his teeth, denying all knowledge of such unneighbourly behaviour. This admittedly ghastly example of family life convinced me that there must be other ways of maintaining some form of discipline without ending up with tiny terrorists, but I did not appreciate how difficult it is until I produced some tiny terrors of my own.

Tantrums

The first tantrum could almost be considered funny, especially if it happens at a particularly tender age. Watching a miniature person throwing her tiny weight around can be highly amusing – for about ten minutes and as long as it is in private. Thereafter it becomes something to be dealt with in the appropriate manner. A lot depends on where it happens. In the privacy of your own home is fine, where ignoring it for as long as possible is usually the best policy. Some parents believe in firm cuddling, where they hold the angry little person close to them. I tried this, but it seemed to frustrate her more and left me rather unhappy, having been firmly punched in the ear. So I took to singing and happily going about my business. Incidentally, I can't sing, so it annoys the screamer even more than being ignored. I can remember one incident where the tantrumer was shrieking 'stop that singing, I'm shouting!' as she writhed about the floor in anger, but in the end I outsang her yelling, and we made up.

Tantrums are scary for children, surprisingly enough, as they reach a point where they can't stop and that feeling of being out of control is terrifying. Some will even go so far as throwing up, or banging their heads on the floor or walls, and that is a good time to intervene, even if you only move them on to a soft rug. For the vomiters, a big towel to wrap them in and a constant stream of quiet chat to calm them is probably the best approach. This is yet another of those situations where being quietly consistent is the key to success, but it is so much easier in the comfort of your own home than in the great outdoors. They never stop overnight but, working on the law of diminishing returns, tantrums will eventually happen less, often as much due to lack of reaction as to increasing maturity. However, you have to be prepared for all your good private work being undone in one nasty public session.

There aren't many of us who can take the public scene in our stride, especially the famous supermarket session which has every saintly spinster in the place either tut-tutting about your lack of discipline or feeling sorry for the offspring of such an obvious monster. The real trouble here is that you can't walk off and leave children, irrespective of how you feel at that moment about possibly even abandoning them for ever, although it does help if you keep them trapped in the trolley. Putting them firmly in the correct seat is the best policy, from both the sanity and safety angle. I once researched an article about child safety, and was horrified to discover that one of the most common injuries inflicted on children who were allowed to rattle about inside trolleys was having their fingernails ripped out on passing shelves, goods and other trolleys. My knees went weak at the thought of it and my children have really suffered as a result, enduring the indignity of being kept firmly in their place until they are at least two and a half. The good side to this is the reduction in possible situations where they can throw a wobbly, because it certainly doesn't have the same impact when they are strapped in place and unable to roll screaming on the floor.

One thing to bear in mind, however, is that this position does leave them in the ideal place to give you a quick kick in the stomach, which is not ideal if you are pregnant again.

Wherever they do it, go for ignoring as your first option. Ignore the child, ignore interested passers-by, ignore everything apart from the business in hand, be it shopping, choosing a book in the library (now that requires a level of calm a sphinx would be proud of!) or wandering in the park. Try and stop your children flinging themselves into ponds or against brick walls, but a roll in mud or a dive into a puddle occasionally won't do anyone any lasting harm. If you have to be somewhere and the tantrum shows no sign of abating, brute force may be required. There is a strange myth about toddlers being helpless little beings, as you will discover when you try to force a rigid small body into a car seat or a buggy. A karate chop to the stomach area is not a good idea; instead, hold her firmly in place with one hand until she stops screaming long enough to draw breath. You now have approximately half a second in which you attempt to push her tummy back with the restraining hand, while fastening a complicated harness with the other. Easy, peasy – or would be if you had a rugby team to help you.

Smacking

The big question which crops up all the time is the smacking issue – do you or don't you? If you do, how do you feel about anyone else doing it to your child? I think this is an issue where you have to have very clear beliefs about whether you actually consider it a useful tool or whether it simply helps you to let off steam when the child has driven you to distraction. Indiscriminate slapping is cruel, confusing and totally unfair but, depending on the child, a swift smack on a well-padded bottom can be just what is needed to stop some unacceptable behaviour getting out of control. We have some very firm guidelines about smacking in our family, but the main rule is that it is used only to prevent the child inflicting damage or injury on themselves or others. You can discuss the dangers of traffic until the cows come home and be ignored by your two-year-old, but a firm smack and equally firm 'No!' every time she attempts to dive under the wheels of a lorry has an instant and lasting effect.

If smacking is considered necessary, I am the one who does the deed, as my husband feels that irrespective of the ages involved, men should never be seen hitting women. I love the politically correct aspect of these beliefs, if only because it doesn't do his image any harm with our daughters, whereas Mummy is always the bad cop. However, we are the only ones allowed to consider smacking our children, and I cannot express how unhappy I would be if child-minders or baby-sitters took it upon themselves to spank my children. Whatever you decide about the smacking issue, it is purely a matter of personal choice, and I would not recommend handing that option to anyone else who cares for your children.

Biting

Biting is a particularly vicious form of assault among small children, and one which they inflict on adults as well as their peers. Dealing with it is traumatic. If you have ever been bitten yourself by a determined small child, you can understand other toddler victims' screaming hysteria. The mother of the child who has been bitten would like to see the perpetrator hung, drawn and quartered, the mother of the assailant would like the ground to open up and swallow her, and there is a general rumpus of hurt crying and guilty roaring. If your child is the biter, remove her firmly from her victim, give her an extremely firm ticking-off and leave her sitting where she can see you as you go back and give all the fuss, cuddles and attention required to the sufferer. Apologise profusely to the anguished parent, even if their little wretch started it all, and be seen to be doing something as you then march your small horror from the scene. It has happened to most of us, it is just about the most painful part of toddler tussles and it cannot be ignored or laughed off.

If your child continues to do it, you are going to have to make it clear that it is the most unacceptable behaviour, irrespective of her age. The youngest children understand disapproving tones, and if they are removed every time they attempt it they will start to get the message, especially if it is from a fun place like toddler group or someone else's toys. For a while you will feel that you have eyes in the back of your head as you keep an endless watch on what is going on, but then the mothers of all the potential victims will be doing likewise, so you will be in good company.

BULLYING

Children will always bicker and fight, even at a very young age, especially before they come to grips with the civilised idea of sharing. It can be quite disconcerting to see babies as young as nine months hang on grimly to each end of a toy, both refusing to relinquish their prize. The chances are that both of them will end up in tears, no matter who wins. We all try to work on a very middle-of-the-road basis, where our child is neither a bully nor a victim, but this can be a difficult balance to achieve. In this country recently there has been a complete about-turn on the subject of bullying. In the past, it was viewed as an intrinsic part of life at school, and you were encouraged either to shut up or put up, neither of which was much use.

Fortunately, these old-fashioned views are dead and being rapidly buried, as are all the misconceptions which went with them. One of the most interesting results of the educational psychologists' research is that bullying tendencies can now manifest themselves as early as eighteen months to two years, and the traditional patterns of bully and victim can be established long before a child reaches school. In our society we also actively encourage the interactive play and learning which is promoted alongside playgroups and nurseries, assuming, usually quite rightly, that we are encouraging our children to mix confidently with their peer groups from an early age. However, without trying to scare anyone, bullying can ruin a child's life and we must be alert to the possibility of it without scaremongering.

The experts' advice is fairly straightforward, asking you at first to consider your child's personality. You might have been Miss Extrovert 1986, while your child is quiet, more introverted and happy with her own company. Tempting though it might be, don't go raking through the elements of your personality which you are not too keen on and then try to prevent them from reappearing in your child, because as a confidence-destroyer that has to be high on the list. Sometimes only subconsciously, but more often consciously, children are uncomfortably aware that if their parents don't love them the way they are, they have got no chance when it comes to the rest of the world. You got them as a package; just love them as they are. Tell them they are smart, and fun, and attractive; praise them up to the skies for being kind, or for sharing, or for singing 'Daisy, Daisy' like no one has ever done before.

That doesn't mean, however, that you turn a blind eye to unacceptable behaviour, but criticise the action, not the child. 'You're a bad boy' might make him think that he is, through and through, whereas 'That was a naughty thing to do' makes it quite clear that it was the behaviour, not the person, that was seen as a problem. There is a world of difference between inane, wishy-washy sentiments and wholehearted praise, and children are anything but daft. I know one mum who simply pretends her son is an angel, and goes on and on about this to the rest of us, in the hope that we are stupid enough to believe her and ignore the monster's latest nasty little ploy. 'He's such a loving little boy,' she coos. 'He's always saying that he's going to stay with me for ever and last week he brought me a bunch of flowers.' Meanwhile she ignores the fact that he is briskly rubbing some other child's face against a rough brick wall.

People like that are blind to any fault in their children, which does the rest of us no favours and has a knock-on effect on the over-adored ones themselves. Children reach an age where they have a very clear idea of exactly what is and what isn't fair, and party invitations eventually become rather thin on the ground for the brat who always creates when she doesn't win every game. At around the time you are gritting your teeth and thinking 'I don't want that child in my house ever again!', your child will come to the same conclusion and calmly tell you that she is no longer friends with so and so. Fine. No problem.

But what do you do if your child is that monster? You need someone like a very close friend, sister or mum who will tell you honestly what they think about the situation. Don't shoot the messenger, especially if you asked for their opinion. Take a hard look at what has precipitated the problem and discuss it with your partner before taking any action, because a united front is vital for this. The thought of your child being unpopular is very hard to come to terms with; this is especially true of young children, because they are still mirroring so much of your own beliefs and behaviour.

Sometimes it has just become too much trouble to maintain any form of discipline, especially if there has been any family upheaval. Giving in has become simpler than standing your ground, or actually putting discipline into effect has become too much of a battle. Children work best with some sort of organised structure, and if that starts falling apart then their automatic panic reaction is to see just how far they can go before their normal life comes back. As parents, it is up to us to provide the stability which helps them face the rest of the world, but no one said it was going to be an easy job. My elder sister once told me that the qualities she wanted her daughters to have when mixing with the rest of society were 'to be independent, assertive and with very good manners'. At home, they could have all the love and encouragement imaginable. I had to think about this for a while, and my eventual conclusion was that it is brilliant in its simplicity.

We can't just abdicate our responsibilities the moment childminders, playleaders and teachers become part of our children's lives, no matter how tempting it might be or how busy we are. Recently there has been a lot of publicity about disruptive children in schools, with teachers refusing to work with them. There was one ten-year-old boy who left me completely baffled. He was cracking chewing gum and striding around with the latest in trendy trainers, baseball cap and surly expression, while his mother whined, 'I blame the school. They shouldn't employ teachers what can't control him.' For the first time in my life I could feel the most shocking right-wing opinions rising up in me, and I wanted to grab her and ask where she thought her responsibilities and control ended.

If we want teenagers who are willing to listen to us occasionally, then we need to start shaping them from babyhood. Mind you, we all want miracles. If we are completely honest, what we would really like for our children runs along these lines. From the moment they can socialise, we want them to be part of the crowd, and that is to continue for the main part of their schooling. We want them to be good-looking, fairly bright but certainly not the school swot, reasonably sporty and an excellent all-rounder. Just as they reach the first of the important exams, in the middle of a hard-working group of like-minded friends, they blossom. Straight As, fabulous looks, popular as ever, and the world's their oyster. Well, you can dream, can't you?

Thinking about Childcare

Coming back to reality, it is time to get organised. Going back to work might still be some time away, but you need to plan well ahead. You have considered all the pros and cons of your child learning to mix with others in different environments, and you are confident that she can cope with your help. All you have to do now is decide what type of childcare is ideal in your situation. The first considerations will centre on how much you can afford to pay, and what you are looking for in your carer. Unfortunately, Britain has the worst state provision of child and nursery care in Europe, so don't expect any substantial government help, either practical or financial, in organising assistance. Perhaps as a direct result of this pathetic omission, relatives are the greatest childcare providers.

Family Assistance

Partners carry the main burden, quickly followed by grandparents, and costs are usually low. The benefits are based around an already close relationship, where you know and trust the carer and your children are assured of an ongoing and loving relationship with them. Difficulties can arise over issues such as partners feeling that they are taken for granted, resentment about not actually earning and, in the case of older relatives, conflicts over methods of discipline and other aspects of childcare. You must look at this as being a long-term plan, and adjust accordingly. If you are going to feel resentful about being indebted, or the carer makes sure you do, or you start to expect too much or don't realise that a grandparent simply isn't fit enough to care for an active child, then the arrangement could well end in tears for everyone.

With partners, you need to discuss the family finances and also all the practicalities of running a home smoothly; if one of you is going to be doing the bulk of the childcare and essentially become a housewife/househusband, then the other will need to make a conscious effort to recognise the value of their contribution, and not just bring everything down to financial terms. With a grandparent, keep an eye on the situation and don't take them for granted. At the outset, make it clear how you want your child to be brought up, but have a little sense when it comes to grandparents' natural tendencies to indulge. The odd piece of chocolate is nothing, whereas overruling your authority in front of the child is a different ball game altogether. If you are uncomfortable about your relatives refusing any payment, try and reach a mutual agreement which helps them, and lets you feel less indebted. You could pay their council tax on a regular basis, pick up their paper bill or do a monthly shop for them. This is not a regular employer/employee relationship so treat with care, because if it works out you couldn't ask for better.

CHILD-MINDERS

Child-minders are the next most popular option. They are registered with social services, who will have checked out every adult in the household and also inspected the home to make sure it is safe, clean and provides all the necessary services needed when caring for small children. There is a limit to the number of children they can care for, which takes into account the size of their own family. The current maximum is three under-fives or five under-eights, and the costs vary wildly from place to place, from as little as £1.50 up to £5.50 an hour.

Child-minders are self-employed, so they deal with their own tax and national insurance, and your child benefits from being in a home environment and learning to mix with other children on a regular basis. The main disadvantage with this system is having to take your child to the child-minder every time you are working, which can require some good organisation and fancy footwork in the morning to ensure that everyone gets to the right place on time every day. Some child-minders can be very inflexible about delays at work which in turn delay you at the end of the day, so make sure that you and she are prepared for this eventuality if it is likely to be a regular occurrence. Your children will undoubtedly get less individual attention and care than they do with you, or if they are someone else's sole charge. You might feel that the company of other children makes up for this, but if you have any concerns, then this is not the best solution for you.

NANNIES

A slightly different approach to this is to have a child-minder who comes to your home and cares exclusively for your child, and as this is similar to having a live-out nanny I will deal with both together. Either your carer will have the necessary experience, or a qualification such as the NNEB. The cost can be a lot more than taking a child to a child-minder, but may work out fairly reasonable if you have more than one child needing to be looked after. You might like to consider nanny-sharing with a friend, especially if you work part-time or job share, but this is another arrangement to be set out very clearly in advance, deciding whose house will be used and so on. Again, prices vary enormously, but for a full-time carer in your own home you can expect to pay anything between £100 and £300 a week, dependent on hours, qualifications and number of children being looked after. You are also responsible for tax and national insurance, which can add a fair amount to your already considerable outgoings, and any reasonable employer will take into account holiday pay, sick pay and overtime.

This is a convenient and flexible arrangement, giving children the benefit of one-to-one attention in the familiar comfort of their own home, while making sure that they are still able to enjoy all socialising activities such as toddler group or 'tumble tots'. As with everything, however, there are potential problems, especially if your nanny is very young and inexperienced or, conversely, so set in her ways that any suggestions by you are considered a gross intrusion. However, please remember that you are employing her to care for your child, not to turn your house into an advert for *Homes and Gardens*. If she is expected to do light housework, such as washing or ironing the children's clothes, make that clear from the beginning. Don't saunter in from work and toss barbed remarks such as 'didn't you have time to turn the washing machine on then?' in her direction. If you want a housekeeper/nanny then advertise for one; don't hire someone in either capacity and expect them to do everything else.

If you decide to go for a live-in nanny, expect to pay between £80 and £200 a week, and be prepared for some loss of privacy. It doesn't matter if you provide the most luxurious bedsitter imaginable – you will still have another adult in the house and will notice all the extras that go with it, including unknown visitors and bigger bills.

In all situations where your child is being cared for primarily by one person, it is very wise to make sure that this person has back-up organised for any emergencies such as her being unwell, because the majority of employers do not take to parents having days off 'sick' to cover for lack of childcare. Furthermore, irrespective of the type of care you go for, what do you plan to do if your child is unwell and so unable to mix with other children? This is the moment where a sympathetic grandparent or an understanding boss is beyond both value and praise, but unfortunately both are rather thin on the ground.

Nurseries
There are many private nurseries around and finding the best one to suit your needs involves a lot of groundwork. On the work front, there are now some more enlightened companies who provide either a crèche or subsidised care. If you have

one, then use it, because the more a need is seen for it, the more likely it is to stay open. If there are certain aspects of it which don't meet your criteria, then talk to other users and staff about possible changes before approaching management. When you do make an approach, make sure that you do not merely come up with a vague litany of complaints; instead, produce a cohesive, realistic game plan for the future, backed up by research and statistics. Combining good parenting with far-reaching careers should be the aim of the next millennium, but it needs input from all sources. Company nurseries are new and should be nurtured so, whatever you do, don't destroy yours through negativity.

Sadly, however, such schemes are very much in the minority, so if you plan to use a nursery, the chances are that you will have to find the best by yourself. They vary considerably in the ages they cater for, although the majority will now take babies from six months onwards, while some will take them even younger. For under-fives, the carer-to-child ratio is one to three for under-twos and one to five for the two-to-five age group, and although it is not a legal requirement, the management in most nurseries prefer their carers to have a recognised qualification. Some will specialise in particular types of education for over-threes, such as the Montessori or Steiner methods, which are a matter of personal preference for parents.

It is impossible to generalise about nurseries, and I suggest you go in for a lot of local research, inspecting places and canvassing opinion from people you know. Reaction to nursery care differs, with some parents feeling that their child is happy and well cared for in a stimulating environment which will provide stability and continuity from infancy to school, while others feel that they smack of institutionalism and rigidity. I'm sorry, but there cannot be a set reply to either of these opinions, as it will all come down to what each nursery provides. You will have to make a decision based on a combination of what is right in front of you and good old instinct. Costs will range from £50 to £200 a week, depending on how many hours you use the nursery for, although many charge by the session and stipulate a minimum use.

Au Pairs

Au pairs provide part-time care, but remember that they are in this country for a number of reasons, and not just to look after children. They must be over 17, can only work for five hours a day – which can include light household duties as well as childcare – and must be given time off for language tuition. They don't have to have any childcare experience, and it is very unlikely that they would have any relevant qualifications, given their age. They live in, and are paid £30 to £50 pocket-money a week. This is not the most continuous type of care – any disagreement, personal problems or straightforward homesickness and they could be gone in a flash. Even if you do all manage to get the balance right, most of them will be in this country for a maximum of a year, so your children will have the instability of developing a relationship, only to have it end and the whole process start again.

Vigilant Checking

Whatever you decide is the best care for you, be as thorough as possible when checking it out, be it an individual or an establishment. Visit child-minders at home to watch them in action, and ask for names of parents of previous charges to take up references. Find out about the little sneaky things which you mightn't be terribly keen on, such as whether anyone ever smokes in the house, or what the normal form of discipline is. Find out what the response would be to an emergency, or what the back-up is in such a situation. The same applies to nannies, and the time to sort everything out is the interview stage. You want to get on with her but you are not looking for a best friend, assuming you already have one of these. You are entrusting these people with the most important person in your life, someone who is too young and too vulnerable to leave anything to chance, and if a prospective carer is going to take umbrage because you would like to see her in action or to take up references, then strike her off the list immediately. Sound practical care is immeasurable, but nothing is as important as knowing that your baby will be loved and cared for. Treat nurseries in the same way, but don't feel under any obligation to skimp on checking every area when confronted by a patronising or know-it-all manager. Come in to see what they do on a daily basis, feel free to look at cots or check highchairs, and don't worry about giving the impression that you are fussy or pernickety. Well, you are, aren't you, where your child is concerned?

Start your childcare three to four weeks before you go back to work, to ensure as smooth a transition as possible, and try to pre-empt any potential problems by having clear guidelines on food, routine, treats and so on. It can come as a shock to realise that you will probably be paying out wages for four to eight weeks before you have a pay-day of your own, so make sure that appropriate funds are set aside to cover this.

So where do you find this modern-day Mary Poppins? The first and best source is word of mouth, especially if you are already involved with other mums and children in the area. Watch how children relate to the adults around them and you will realise very quickly which particular child-minders appeal to them. It is not going to be the most easily walked-over, strangely enough, but the one who talks to them, enjoys their company and relates well to their lives. There is an entire generation of toddlers growing up around here whose attitude to child-minders is summed up in the one assessment: 'If I ever have to get a child-minder I only want Gillian.' The only problem with this is that Gillian is happily settled with the three little sisters she has looked after since the first was born, which leaves a very disappointed crowd of prospective employers and petulant tinies who don't understand that she isn't easily reproduced. Trust your instincts, and if you don't have the right feeling about someone, then don't employ her. If your partner is tempted to stay out of all these negotiations, persuade him to get involved, as the two of you should be equally determined to provide the best possible solution for everyone.

STATE NURSERIES

Alongside all these types of care, there are also local playgroups and state nurseries which you may well wish to use, but because of the limited hours these are available for you are more likely to use them in conjunction with your usual care methods. Playgroups are usually privately run, and on the basis of a group of parents getting together to form a group which raises its own funds to employ playleaders. All the children within a group will be entitled to three or four sessions a week, for two to three hours each time. These sessions will involve lots of interactive play, dancing, more contemplative play such as jigsaws or puzzles, story-time, dressing-up, painting and a whole host of all those other pursuits so dear to children's hearts. This is a lovely introduction to nursery, and usually involves a gentle breaking-in period until your child is quite confident to stay without Mum, Granny or the child-minder. There will be fundraising events which can be surprisingly good fun, and the usual system will involve paying a small registration fee of £10 to £20, and then paying on a monthly or termly basis for allocated sessions, which can range from £1 an hour upwards.

Having only had experience of one state nursery I am not really in the best position to give a qualified opinion – but that has never stopped me in the past. For the record, I thought it was excellent, from the care, tact and sheer cuddliness of the staff in settling in over 30 rather apprehensive small people (and their even more apprehensive parents) to giving them good preparation for attending school, both educationally and practically. Local authority nurseries should be available to all, but despite the much vaunted nursery vouchers and government propaganda, the reality is depressing. Where I live, you are almost guaranteed a place for pre-school year, and are definitely given one if you are a single parent, there are social problems in the home or English is not your first language. The current charge is £3 a week for five full mornings or afternoons if either partner is working, and £1 a week if you are not receiving a wage, or are on benefit of any kind.

Just ten minutes' walk away, however, there is no local authority nursery available, and regardless of whether you are a single parent of six, unable to utter a word of English or cope with a difficult home situation, you have two chances of a nursery place – fat or thin. The situation is unfair, unworkable and unjustifiable, if only because the advantages of good pre-school education go far beyond that first year in laying the sort of foundations which will have positive benefits throughout the child's entire school life. If you are in an area which doesn't provide state nursery places, then think about developing a very loud voice about it long before your child's pre-school year. Lobby councillors, MPs and anyone else whose job depends on the people they represent, and get other parents into action with you. Despite constant cuts in public spending and the systematic dismantling of our excellent education service, it is still there for the use of the public at large, who need to make their views regarding its future known.

SCHOOLS

I will now retire from my soapbox to get on to the subject of schools. More than anything, this will make you feel that you are truly a grown-up member of society. Suddenly, you realise that when you moved to your present abode it was as an unencumbered adult, and the most pressing concern about its locality was whether or not it was within walking distance of the pub. In less than five years you will have to think seriously about educating your tiny babe and, before you know it, the proximity of The Queen's Head does not have the same importance as previously. Some parents will automatically opt for independent schooling, assuming that their funds will stretch. One word of caution, if this is your plan. Cost not only the fees and the uniform, but remember all the extras which can crop up over the years, especially if you plan a large family. You will have to make sure that all members receive the same quality of education, and take peer pressure into account. This is part of life in every school, but while it is true that some parents work themselves into the ground to pay for their children's education, it is also true that there will be pupils in the school who receive more in pocket-money than some people do in wages and, life being what it is, some will delight in flaunting it.

If you can, refrain from criticising other people for the decisions they make about their children's schooling, especially if you are the lucky sort of ranting socialist who lives in a good area and therefore has the chance of using an excellent local state school. Speaking as a previously ranting socialist, I would suggest that you accept that parenthood can change all of us and our principles overnight, and if someone then wants to work every hour to buy the best education or health care they can find for their children, then I for one will leave them in peace to do so. Buying your home in a 'good' area is almost exactly the same thing, except you can justify it by saying, 'Well, all state schools should be as good as this one.' They aren't, and they are certainly not going to change overnight, so what do you do – sacrifice your children for your principles? Unlikely in the majority of cases, so go for the best you can while actively supporting education everywhere.

Getting involved in the system for the first time can be a little daunting, as school policy changes from area to area. When your baby is about six weeks old and you cannot fail to miss the natural brilliance emanating from every pore, you start to think about nurturing this genius. Once you have decided which would be the best place to bring this creativity to fruition, contact the school and ask about waiting lists, place availability and catchment areas. Never assume that you will automatically get a place in the school of your choice, so make sure you have an acceptable Plan B if the first doesn't come off. It may seem like a long way down the line, but before you know it you could find yourself weeping pathetically over tiny uniforms. If this talk of school makes you realise that you will have to start actively contemplating a house move in the next couple of years, it is as good a time as any for considering your career options.

Chapter Seven

Going Back to Work

An eternity ago, when you were first contemplating pregnancy or had first conceived, your baby fitted in neatly with your great life plan. After an initial period of readjustment, everything would slot neatly into place, including this brand new member of your family. Maybe you tried to calculate the financial cost, working out travel, child-minding and even nappies against your pay-slip, but it is highly unlikely that you had the slightest idea of the impact one tiny person could make on a well-ordered and adult life. Maternity leave can suddenly stop being a pleasant hiatus before resuming normal service, and you start ticking off the days in dread as the date approaches for your return to work. Maybe you are actually looking forward to resuming your career, but dread the organisation involved to get it all running smoothly.

FORWARD PLANNING

First of all, let us consider your original idea for returning to work full-time, and assume that is still the plan. There have been no major hitches in your absence, maternity leave cover has been well organised and effective, and all that remains is for you to take up your place again. That is optimistic at best, and at worst totally unrealistic. Even if you took the minimum maternity leave you will have been away from work for three months, and a lot can change in that short period of time. When you have fixed a date for returning to work, arrange a time before that date when you can go in to work for a few hours to do a kind of refresher course. Make sure that it is a convenient day to see everyone with whom you will have regular contact, especially your immediate supervisor, and have a thorough session with whoever has been covering your maternity leave, concentrating on any recurring problems or innovations which will affect you directly.

The last time your colleagues saw you was probably when you brought your baby in for them to admire, when you were flushed with pride and joy and possibly swaying with exhaustion. Forget that image. You are about to step into your work persona, so resist the temptation to regale everyone in sight with delightful childhood tales, no matter how often they ask or how interested they seem. Personal lives are best kept for tea breaks and lunchtimes, especially since half the males in the office, and a lot of cynical females, will expect you to have turned into the fluffy bunny mumsy type.

Don't turn up in cereal-stained leggings and your oldest breast-feeding T-shirt but don't feel you have to take up power-dressing either, so go for smart and casual. Familiarise yourself with any changes in routine or procedure, make copies of any relevant paperwork which you can take away with you and mug up, and then go home and if necessary cry your eyes out because your beloved career is nothing in the face of your feelings for your precious baby. This may well be true, but it is possible that you might be the sort of person who has to give it time to get some sort of grip on you again, while others instantly feel that heady rush of adrenalin at being in control and can't wait to get back in there. This could be a direct reaction to all the months when they felt a tiny baby was in control instead, but if it works, then who cares?

If you are looking forward to going back to work this will obviously make the transition of the first few weeks more bearable, but even if you are contemplating it with fear and loathing you will have to prepare for it in the same way. The easiest way of getting your mornings organised from the point of view of childcare is if your carer is coming to your home, but whichever method you have chosen, it will require fairly meticulous organisation. As far as possible do it the night before – and that means both of you, instead of you rushing about like a demented bee as your partner relaxes with a beer and the remote control. Iron clothes and organise packed lunches or the baby's changing bag the night before, and if you have a mind like the proverbial sieve, stick a list on to the front door to check before leaving, or line everything up in the hall so you can't possibly get out without tripping over it all.

Get some routine into mornings so that they work like clockwork; your partner could start by feeding himself and the baby while you transform yourself into a vision of radiant beauty (although passable will also do at a push), get suitably dressed for work and then cover yourself from neck to toe in your dressing-gown. This is simply to stop Sod's Law ruining your day, the first rule clearly stating that the moment you are immaculately clad your baby will pour cereal down you, or maybe throw up on your silk blouse, just to show you who's boss. Then swap roles: you eat and then get the baby ready, while your partner gets to grips with his ablutions.

If everything goes according to plan you will all be heading out the door in good time, bright-eyed and bushy tailed, and you might even have got as far as throwing the dirty dishes into the sink. Things are rarely that simple, however. A broken night, the temptation to act like grown-ups for once and stay up late drinking wine, or all the thousands of tiny things that can go wrong in the morning will invariably make the start of the day frantic and irritating. If you can bear to leave your lovely bed it is almost worth getting up ten minutes earlier than you have to, just to try and stay on top of things. If you don't mind a mad scramble in the mornings then forget I ever said that, but a lot of us find the rest of the day ruined if we start off by rushing around like a scalded cat.

GETTING BACK INTO THE ROUTINE

In work, try to slide back into the routine as quickly as possible, because no allowances are made. It is easier in some ways to pretend that nothing has changed for the first few weeks, no matter how much of an effort you have to make to sustain this impression, because there is nearly always someone waiting for you to reveal the fragility of working mothers. I have never come up with a satisfactory explanation for this, because all the working mothers I know – myself included – have a lot more to prove now we have children. It is not just about the now desperate need for hard cash to squander on things like food and shoes, but a somewhat more complicated set of reasons. Naturally money is part of it, and alongside that we almost have to provide good reasons for what we are doing, as if we were still stuck in some Neanderthal age where we had no automatic right to any form of equality. It might drive us mad, but we still have to justify every area in our lives by being better than the chap next to us who is doing the same job.

Some of it we bring on ourselves, as would be evident if anyone could be bothered to do a quick survey comparing what parents do in their lunch hours. I would put my money on the men having lunch, while the women do a panic-stricken shop and try and organise that evening's meal. Sorry, but you will get no sympathy from this quarter if you treat your partner like some helpless child instead of an equal when you are both putting the same effort into running your family – either speak up or put up with it. That apart, it is true that your career can lose impetus and credibility when you become a mother, but it is extremely disheartening when you are confronted by such outdated views. It further complicates matters when you realise that much as you loved your job before, it now plays a very poor second fiddle to your child. That's just life, and I am sure that every man you ask would say the same – but no one expects him to jack in his job just because he loves his child.

Some people are extremely good at putting, and keeping, everything in its own separate compartment, so they are able to switch roles smoothly, without a backward glance. Most of us aren't so tidy, however, and emotions can be very complicated. If you have spent the latter part of your maternity leave dying to get back to real life and then find that you are spending a good part of your working day pining for your baby and driving the child-minder and your colleagues mad with constant phone calls to check that she is coping without you, it all comes as a bit of a shock. One very high-powered executive I worked with came back to work when her daughter was six weeks old, and later confessed to me that she spent the first 20 minutes of her lunch hours expressing milk, the second 20 minutes sobbing silently in the loo because she was missing her baby so much, and the remainder of the time doing a perfect make-up job to repair the damage. This from a woman who worked until the week of giving birth, was back in her size 10 suits a month later, and is in charge of a workforce of over 10,000. She has no regrets about the way she chose to have a family, but hadn't bargained on the old hormones getting in on the act. Even the photograph of her daughter which she had proudly displayed on her desk had to be banished for a couple of months, until she learned to look at it without bursting into tears!

WORK-INDUCED STRESS
It can be hard enough to return to a job which you enjoy and

want to carry on with, but if you are working only because you have to, hate your job or would give anything to be at home with your baby, then the pressures can become unbearable. If you have been with the same company or line of work for years, then you can't help but feel some measure of security, and the thought of giving up a regular wage can be very daunting. Sometimes you find yourself working only to keep a job for yourself for the future, because once you add up all your childcare costs and incidentals which go with returning to the workplace you can be left with very little at the end of the month. However, there is no doubt that irrespective of how little you gain financially your career status remains intact, providing some promise of employment long after your children are grown up, and this is a situation many people find well-nigh impossible to give up, no matter how miserable they might be.

If you decide that you have to stick it out, even just to ensure that you will be entitled to another bout of maternity leave in the future, then try to remain as cheerful as possible while doing so. You do nothing for your professional image or self-esteem if you make it clear to all and sundry that you are in the workplace under duress, and while colleagues might be sympathetic initially they soon get fed up with the Moaning Minnie scenario. It can also have a nasty knock-on effect on any promotions, as no bosses in their right mind will offer you a better post while you whine and moan about your present one. Your partner could do with a reasonably cheerful face to look at too, so there is no point in grinding him down at the end of every day with a litany of complaints which no one can do anything about. The bottom line is that apart from a few lucky lottery winners we are all in the same leaky boat, having to work for a living. Why should you expect special treatment, just because you are now a parent?

CONSIDERING NEW OPTIONS

On the other hand, nothing is ever set in stone, whether job prospects, security or long-term plans. If the situation you have returned to is causing real dissatisfaction, it is time to reconsider your options. This is a fine exercise in going round in circles, so I would suggest actually noting down the pros and cons of each solution. Comparing the difference in income between working full or part time can be surprising, assuming that your childcare costs would now be almost halved. Unless you are a particularly high earner you should find that in hard cash terms there will be very little difference, and this might be the answer to your problems. More and more people are working part time or job sharing, and some couples have even managed to secure this in both their jobs, thereby neatly dovetailing childcare and giving them equal input into family finances. While you are busy working out how to approach your employer, don't forget your child-minder, who mightn't be too keen on having her income halved. Consider her options along with your own, as the situation could result in her looking after another child part time or – horror of horrors, after all you went through to find her – handing in her notice and leaving you to start from scratch.

Before you do approach your personnel department, find out as much as possible about company policy on job sharing, which is usually a lot fairer and more secure than part-time work. So far, job sharing has had a very good press, due in the main to the determination of those involved to make it work. Although originally used by far more women than men, this is no longer necessarily the case, and you tend to find that if companies have been prepared to let men get involved and found that it – and they – work well, then the concept is embraced wholeheartedly. Look at your aims for the future and how far each person's career can reasonably go before deciding which of you would like to give up some of your work time to be the primary carer.

If job sharing is an entirely new concept to your employer, do a lot of relevant research before presenting the idea. Look at similar work which already employs sharers, and be prepared to present the benefits of the scheme. Don't float it as a vague idea, but as a polished concept, embracing areas such as holidays, sick pay and staff training. Show willingness to adapt as the scheme is introduced, and be willing to help in training your co-sharer, or at least in showing him or her the ropes. You might suggest an overlap of a few hours each week to start with, to expedite the smooth introduction of an entirely new way of working. A couple of words of warning: you are not asking for any favours as such, so don't be too humble. You are simply suggesting that your company recognise the value of job sharing to retain an excellent workforce and to stay in step with what is now seen as a beneficial exercise, particularly when it comes to combining effective parenting with a profitable career. Always remember that you have another option, which is taking your skills and expertise to a more forward-looking company.

It may come as another little surprise, but remaining in the recognised workforce is not the only option. Parenthood is full of contradictions, and nowhere more so than in the area of work. Once you get past the idea that you have already found all the security you could ever want, you can discover an entirely new sense of freedom regarding retraining, a total change of career, or even a sideways or downwards move more suited to your present domestic situation. Having done this myself I am convinced that there are two main reasons behind this unexpected bravery. Firstly, I had no idea that becoming a parent would instantly fill me with a burning desire for immortality, or at least the hope of living to a very healthy old age. With this as my main ambition, it made perfect sense to embrace a career which I wholeheartedly loved, as opposed to one which I merely tolerated, considering that it would affect the whole quality of my life and make it more likely that I would celebrate my century.

Secondly, there is a perfect confidence which gradually fills you as you become more used to being a parent and coping with everything which could affect your child's health or happiness in some way. I don't mean the sort of confidence which enables you to change a dirty nappy in a moving car, breast feed anywhere or argue with stroppy receptionists over the fact that your child needs to see a doctor now, although all these skills are admirable. This confidence comes with the responsibility of caring for a tiny person whom you would literally die for, and it translates into a belief in yourself and your abilities which you have never before experienced or had any desire to put into action. It doesn't make it easy to give up a full-time job for the great unknown, but in my case my desire to be the one caring for my daughter far outweighed the feeling that I should stick with the old familiar ways. It was a good instinct, but was backed up by a supportive husband, hard work and a brass neck. Freelancing has expanded my career, provided me with work opportunities and experiences I could only have dreamed of, and given me the time with my children which I so desperately wanted. There have been some rather hairy moments, such as staying up half the night to meet a deadline and waiting in disbelief for nearly three months for an invoice to be settled, but nobody promised that it would be easy.

A Total Change

If becoming self-employed or working from home appeals to you, then step back and take a long, hard look at all the skills you have to offer, and what you can utilise to allow you to pursue something new. That may sound a little confusing, but it basically means not only assessing your concrete qualifications such as specialised training or degrees, but also considering hobbies and interests which you have never considered in the light of profit-making. Be careful when it comes to traditional home-working, and make sure you work out to the last penny exactly what you will be paid. If I sound cynical it is because I have seen far too many of those 'make over £200 a week in your spare time' adverts, an achievement which is only feasible if you have over 200 spare hours a week to accomplish this in, and nobody would consider the resulting £1 an hour to be a fair wage.

One possible adaptation is to continue to do your present job but to do it from home, and the first place to start with such an idea is your personnel section, to determine whether your firm already has a policy on home-working. There is a traditional bias against it in some firms, which seems unlikely to change. This is normally and unfortunately based on the idea that if you are out of sight then you are not working, an idea which presents a totally false image of what home-workers actually do. Naturally, there are some jobs which would be impossible to transfer to the home because the place of work is an important part of what is done. However, pioneering companies do exist – usually falling into particular types such as financial, media or telecommunications – so you may find you get a sympathetic hearing, especially if it has already been shown to work successfully in your field.

Think about your own personality in relation to commitment, being able to discipline yourself and having the ability to work without constant supervision. Any equipment provided by your office would need to be updated and maintained to the same standard as that in the office itself, and you would have to make sure that from the outset there was some system of communication which prevented either isolation or failure to do the job correctly. If the work would have to be done in office hours, don't imagine that it would be possible to do so as your baby gurgles at your feet. Get childcare organised before you start to revolutionise current work systems.

Professional Help

When it comes to branching out on your own, finance and the best advice are the main criteria. Enterprise Allowance still exists, although under different names in different areas, and I would suggest tracking it down in whatever form it exists in your area and having a chat with one of the counsellors. I don't care how often it is claimed that the counsellors are all recruited under much the same criteria countrywide, because it will be total luck as to who you end up with for help and advice. Having written a number of articles on further education, training and setting up in business, including detailing grants and funding available, I find the diversity of skills and assistance in those who are meant to be trained to help in these situations unbelievable.

I interviewed two women who had set up separately in business for themselves, both in a traditional crafts field. By coincidence they had approached the same office for help in the same week, seen two different counsellors and received completely different assistance. Both were entitled to an Enterprise Allowance grant, which they eventually got, but there the similarity in treatment ended. One counsellor investigated European funding, helped her client secure a £5,000 non-returnable grant, and found subsidised premises to set up her business. For the next year she kept in touch regularly, passing on useful information and contacts including an introduction to a self-employed businesswomen's group which effectively doubled her client's outlets, and helping her to investigate further funding to expand the business.

Meanwhile, the other counsellor did precisely nothing, and although her client had some success, it was entirely due to her own hard work and private funding which she will be paying back for a long time to come. There is help out there, and valuable advice and guidance, but some of those who are meant to come up with the goods are too comfortable in their own jobs to put in the slightest extra effort. What is interesting is the reaction if you cover some of these enterprises for the press, as all the slowcoaches suddenly become vibrant, forward-thinking individuals!

I am sorry to sound so negative, but if you don't warm to your counsellor, try to find someone else. A very useful exercise is to find people who have already used the avenues you will be going down before you actually make any official contacts, which will prevent any embarrassing situations as you try to find someone more helpful. Since so much home-working tends to be based around traditional crafts, the first place to go is a craft fair. Check the local papers for locations, get there early, ask people how they got started, and wait for the same names or agencies to crop up with positive responses. Although it might be perceived as inverted sexism, many places now have very active women's groups which are another good contact, as they focus on giving women the confidence to move into traditionally male-dominated areas. Further-more, they do tend to have an awareness of the problems of finding good childcare and some provide crèches or play areas, which obviously makes life easier if you are accompanied by small children while on this information-seeking drive.

When considering self-employment you need to decide the hours you will work and how this affects the childcare you will need. Money, as ever, can be a real hassle, especially if you anticipate shelling out regular wages long before you start coining it in. All small businesses have complaints about the length of time some creditors take to pay, and it can be very time-consuming and expensive to pursue outstanding debts. It doesn't help you or your child-minder if you owe her £150 a week and are still to receive £1,000 due three weeks ago. Your financial worries have nothing to do with your child-minder and it is unprofessional to involve her – and even more unreasonable to expect her to wait.

WORKING FROM HOME

The idea of working from home is very exciting, especially the concept of fitting this work around doing your own childcare. Some jobs are adaptable, such as book-keeping, cake-making or writing, but no matter how much of the actual grind can be done while your children are asleep, you are going to have to touch base at some point during the normal nine to five day. This is when problems can arise if you have not anticipated just what can go wrong.

The cardinal sin is sounding unprofessional, no matter how professional the finished product is. For example, it doesn't matter to my editors that I work from home, doing the bulk of my writing during evenings and weekends. They need to speak to me during the day, however, outlining articles, deadlines and ideas, and irrespective of how much the work is based around family or human-interest issues, the last thing they need is to hear my family being over-interested in the background. Invest in an answering machine, which will earn its keep remarkably quickly. Make sure you keep your message short and simple, and always return calls as soon as possible. As a back-up to this I recently got a mobile phone, simply to ensure that I could always be reached in an emergency – such as a well-paid interview needing to be written immediately, or possibly sooner. As yet I am unsure how valuable this is. It has certainly ensured that I have got various commissions, but every time I answer it I am either being intimidated by a helicopter, which does nothing for the sound quality, or in a loo somewhere. If there is a queue I feel like a pretentious yuppy, and if it is empty there is a strange echo which leaves me convinced that my caller knows exactly where I am!

Use your answering machine properly, and you will rarely be caught sounding like a harassed mother who couldn't organise a bun fight in a bear pit. Return calls when your children are safely engrossed in something else, and once they are old enough, make it quite clear that work phone calls are out of bounds when it comes to shrieking interruptions. If, like most children, they are utterly determined to answer the phone, make it an unbreakable rule that they are polite – absolutely no one could take offence at a three-year-old saying 'hello, who's calling please?' or 'hold on'. Long chatty conversations with reluctant customers are definitely out, however, as are screamed demands to allow them to sing down the line. You could have a separate phone line put into the house, but if your children are going to be around anyway it seems a bit of an unnecessary expense. Save the money until they are teenagers, when a separate line will become vital if you want to have any business at all.

Once you have decided the area of work you intend to develop and have found the professionals who are ready and able to help you get started, there are still some considerations before you are finally up and running. The first is the simplest. Is your scheme financially viable, and, if not, where can you make changes? It is a common mistake to think that your present home is not big enough, organised enough or even tidy enough to see clients in, but it is a mistake that can cost you a lot of money. Premises are expensive to rent, and most landlords like long-term leases. Play safe, and assume that you will not have large amounts of spare cash to start with. Reorganise a room to allow yourself a fixed station where you can keep ongoing work without always having to tidy it away; the kitchen table may be the most comfortable place in your house but you will quickly get tired of bundling everything away at every mealtime.

If your work involves seeing clients on a regular basis you will have to have a suitable consulting room, especially if you are providing a service such as beauty therapy or dressmaking. One alternative to renting premises is to convert a shed or garage, but this will require considerable outlay to ensure that the finished product reflects a comfortable business, rather than a shoestring affair. However, assuming that the conversion is of a high standard, with good heating and lighting facilities, this would obviously be a sound long-term investment. There are tax benefits to using a room in your home for business as well as some other function, which you would naturally forego if you had a separate room for business only. However, there are some professions where you will have no option but to ensure a private space, and financial planning will need to take such an eventuality into account.

MARKET RESEARCH

If you are convinced that you can provide a viable service, your next step is to do the market research to prove this, especially if you are going to have to draw up any sort of business plan for potential backers. Market research can also prevent expensive mistakes which can determine the success or failure of your business from very early days. To start with, you are hoping to establish that someone wants to buy your product and, furthermore, that this will not be a one-off, but that there will be a continuous market. There are various ways of going about this depending on your product, but all require a lot of groundwork. Questionnaires are always recommended, but expect the response to be very disappointing, considering the effort you need to put in in drawing up the document, copying, distributing and eventually analysing and assessing the information. They are, however, a particularly useful tool once you have established a bank of regular clients, if only to ensure that you receive a constant feedback which will hopefully stop you from becoming complacent or sloppy. Networking is another buzzword, basically meaning keeping up to date with your subject through trade events and journals, and should help you discover any gaps in the market or areas which are about to undergo major changes from which you could benefit.

You cannot afford to price yourself out of the market, but neither can you sell yourself short. If you are providing quality work then expect to be paid at the appropriate rate. You might want to start off by cutting prices while you get yourself established, but bear in mind that it might not be quite so easy to implement a price rise. Remember incidentals while costing a job – there is no point in being well paid for a project if you forget to charge for something like substantial travel which could eat into your profits. Sometimes, in the delight of getting commissions, your common sense can disappear and you can find yourself agreeing to the strangest things. If you are offered a fee of £200 for an article you are writing but then find you have signed a contract agreeing that you will pay the photographer for the accompanying pictures, you are effectively kissing your fee goodbye. Find out what the going rate is, and honestly assess whether the quality of your work deserves that. If not, update your standards before you lose custom and your business.

Friends and acquaintances can provide a good boost in helping get your business off the ground, as word-of-mouth recommendation cannot be bettered when it comes to advertising a quality product. But, and this is a big but, it is worth your while explaining at the outset that this is a business venture, not a pleasant hobby. My sister's business is making fabulous novelty cakes and exquisite wedding cakes, and I have lost count of the number of people who expect her to make them one for the cost of the ingredients alone, simply because they are on first-name terms with her. Don't these people realise that she might have spent six hours creating a fairy castle, or do they think that artistic satisfaction helps pay the bills? I have yet to meet an editor who suggests I write an article for the sake of friendship alone! Perfect the art of a winning smile and a realistic price quote at the same time, prefixed if necessary by 'I'd love to reduce it further, but I have already deducted my profit . . .' Making them feel guilty should prevent you having to do this a second time, but if you would like to show gratitude to those supporting your business venture, do so by presenting them with as perfect a job as you can manage, which will result in satisfaction all round.

Realising that your instincts were right and that you do have a very marketable skill is a heady experience, and at the risk of being a kill-joy I would suggest that you try not to get carried away, especially when it comes to taking on too much and risking not being able to fulfil commitments. We have all been at the mercy of small businesses which have simply taken on too much, and whether it was through greed or a reluctance to turn away clients is irrelevant. The end result is the same: the classic of trying to please everyone and pleasing no one. It doesn't matter if your house has been beautifully refurbished, or your new central heating installed with the minimum of mess – if you had to pester your contractor to get the job finished by the original date or were still chasing him up about details six months later, that is the last time you will use that particular company. Some work has a sell-by date, such as needing a wedding cake or flower arrangements, but others can be more flexible, with an offer to do the job at a slightly later stage. It is far better for your image to be perceived as in demand and reliable, rather than scatty and slapdash. Maybe all your potential customers need is an assurance that with a little more notice you can certainly come up with the goods, but you consider them too important to provide a shoddy service.

As with every rule, however, there has to be the occasional exception, and you can guarantee that one day you will be offered a plum of a commission which you couldn't refuse in a thousand years. This invariably happens when you already have a diary bursting at the seams, a house which resembles the scene of an explosion and your children in bed with something like chicken-pox. But this will be a job you have been waiting for since you started your business, and it will give you the experience and contacts you have always wanted, so do you turn it down? You might be sensible but you are not completely stupid, so by staying up all night, ignoring your sick children beyond a quick cuddle, forcing both your best friend and Granny to look after your home and letting everything else go by the board, you do it. One gin and tonic later you are asleep fully dressed on top of your bed, only to be wakened by the phone ringing. Completely disorientated by exhaustion and the fact that your toddler is sitting on your face, you manage a coherent reply. It is your new customer, delighted with your work and hoping they hadn't put you under too much pressure. So you lie through your teeth and say 'no, honestly, any time, I enjoyed it', then put the phone down and roll about hysterically giggling with your mystified children. It was madness to accept and under no circumstances would you attempt it every week, but just for once it was great to prove to yourself that you could do it.

The mention of planning permission can induce a nervous reaction in the calmest individual, especially as it covers one of these grey areas which no one seems able to give definitive advice about. If you are typing, tutoring or doing research at home the neighbours are unlikely to suffer any drastic change to their lives, but if you start repairing cars in the street or set up a pavement café they will undoubtedly notice, and very possibly object. Consider three main questions as the criteria for needing planning permission. Will your home no longer be used mainly as a private residence? Will your business result in a noticeable increase of people and/or traffic? Will your business disturb your neighbours in any way? If the answer is 'yes' to one or more of these questions, the chances are that you will need to obtain planning permission first.

There are some jobs which necessitate your home being used in the business, such as running a Bed and Breakfast or becoming a child-minder. If you fancy yourself as a landlady, contact your local tourist board for further information. They will give you the most up-to-date advice on any necessary changes to your home and how to become part of a recognised organisation. It is far better to start off as a small but quality establishment rather than going for too big, too soon, unless you have access to large amounts of ready cash. Furthermore, if you gradually build up the business you will quickly develop a sound sense of exactly how much you can cope with easily, and when you have to start cutting corners and reducing the quality of service. Registered child-minders have to meet strict criteria, and there is a limit to the number of children they can care for, including their own.

Some people are simply ideal as child-minders, with the sort of caring yet firm personality that children adore and respond well to, but it is not a job for the faint-hearted. If you mind terribly about your house becoming in any way untidy, don't stay calm in a crisis or are unable to do half a dozen things at once, then don't even consider it. There is a strange myth about child-minding being an easy job, yet nothing could be further from the truth. Think about how you will entertain the children on wet days, when they are trying to pull each others' heads off, and how you will cope with the crowd when it comes to school pick-ups or even just walks to the local park. Consider all the hidden extras you might have to shell out for, such as providing food and drink throughout the day, and adjust your rates accordingly. Sort out with the parents in advance who supplies what, and have a clear policy on holidays and sick days, making sure that you have some sort of emergency back-up. However, this has become the perfect solution for many women who want to be at home with their children while still earning, and provides an excellent service for so many other parents. It is important not to think of it as a casual little job with very little effort required, because you will be both disappointed and exhausted before the first week is over.

Child-minding is usually a straight eight to six job, which does provide an ideal safety net finance-wise if you want to gain further qualifications at night classes with a view to an entire change of career. Good child-minders are greatly in demand, and if you are apprehensive about giving up a steady job to retrain, this might be the best way to do it. Not many of us can afford to give up work completely for a few years to study and this is a workable compromise, although nobody can promise that you won't be exhausted half the time!

TIME OUT
The final option regarding work is to give it all up completely for a few years while you concentrate all your energies into your family, and for many couples this does turn out to be their favoured solution. If one of you earns enough money to support the family and cover all the bills then you are laughing, but that is not always the case. Some people simply accept that to enable one parent to stay at home with the children they will just have to live on the breadline for the next few years, considering it a worthwhile sacrifice. Some employers, notably local authorities and banks, have a scheme where you can take what amounts to a five-year

sabbatical, with the guarantee of a job at the same grade on your return. This is a very reassuring way of keeping your options open. Facing five years of poverty is much easier when you know that you have good earning potential at the end of it.

If you have decided to manage on one wage, then any chance to make a little extra money is always welcome, and at certain times of the year there will be seasonal work which can fit around the main wage-earner's hours and provide some much needed extras. Local supermarkets and shops may need evening or night-time workers, and if you have a recognised qualification such as nursing you could try getting one or two nights a week on a regular basis. Since you then have to spend the following day looking after your children it is another compromise rather than an easy option, but there are lots of people out there doing it. They include a friend of mine, and the next day you can watch her on automatic pilot until she puts the children to bed at 7 p.m. and herself at 7.01 p.m. If you are having a particularly dull day it is worth while trying to have a conversation with her, because her brain is so befuddled it is not unlike listening to *The Goon Show*. I think it's terrific: she's happy, her children are ecstatic and she unwittingly entertains all her friends at the same time!

Whatever you decide to do about your work, one thing is true – it is really only a short-term solution. Before you know it your children will be half-grown and almost civilised, and you will start looking at the last few years in bewilderment. Make the best decision for your family and, if you can, put time with your children first. How you do this will manifest itself in different ways, so don't justify and don't explain. If you feel better working full time and then revelling in every other minute spent with your family, then go for it, but if you prefer to put a high-powered career on hold for a few years and play in the park, then that is an equally good solution, as is every other one in between. No matter what you choose someone will criticise, but remember that it won't be your children. They love you no matter what, as you do them, so who could ask for more?

Chapter Eight

Money Worries

Long, long ago, at the very beginning of this book, I suggested taking a practical look at your finances and trying to work out the impact a baby would have on them. It is a bit like asking 'what would you do if you were the last person left on earth?' because it is practically impossible to judge until you are in the middle of the situation. Small children are an expensive luxury, even if doting grandparents have helped with the initial outlay needed to acquire the necessary pram, cot, bath and everything that goes with them. People you hardly know are really kind to you when you have a baby and the loveliest little gifts appear from unexpected quarters, making you realise that it is not just the immediate family who benefit from a new arrival.

Educating Children about Money

Before I get totally involved in the subject of money, I would like to make it clear that this is not going to be a doom-and gloom-filled account of how having children can plunge you into penury. Instead, I shall look at the realities of juggling a tight budget, but above all there is one thing I want to be totally clear about. At the end of the day it is only money, and while it would be nice to have lots and it is impossible to manage without some, there is not enough in the world to pay for the feelings you get when you hold your children. You want to give them everything, and at times it is disappointing and frustrating when you cannot even afford to buy them a toy, but nothing compares to the love you give them. As they get older you will undoubtedly be taken to task because the boy across the road gets everything his material little heart desires, but that's life. There will always be someone who has more than you, just as there will always be someone who has less, but part of your job as a parent is to help your children understand the different standards and develop some awareness of what is truly important. You are doing your children no favours at all if they grow up thinking they only have to ask in order to get something, with no effort or appreciation in return.

We have all been through that delightful teenage stage where we thought only of ourselves, but it still makes me cringe when I hear some sulky 15-year-old demanding the £140 trainers, although she must surely have some idea that if she gets them her dad's leaking shoes will have to last another two months. Perhaps I will be eating my words when my children reach that stage, but I would like to think that we will have taught them to view the family as a unit where everyone has equal importance, so we don't have a tribe of greedy little wretches who think that their parents' only function is to dole out the cash. It probably helps that my husband and I both come from large families where sharing was a way of life and not some polite option. There were undoubtedly times where we felt hard done by when our parents couldn't afford things like school trips abroad, but we had a fair idea of just how much extra cash there was and what it would be spent on. My dad is a minister and their wages are little more than pocket-money, so causing a scene for something just wasn't on – strangely enough, my parents preferred to feed the family than send a moaning brat to France on holiday! However, we were never short of love, security and encouragement, which in turn gave us unbeatable confidence.

Here endeth the lesson for today but I think it is worth

bearing in mind, especially when your children reach the age of around four and start to get some sense of how much everything costs. The pocket-money ritual can start at around that age, and it is fun for children to save up for something they really want. I was very keen to start this when my elder daughter reached her fourth birthday, and she duly saved up until she had enough money for the deeply desired doll's highchair from the Early Learning Centre. In she went, clutching a purse bulging with coins, and she counted out every one painfully slowly to the patient woman at the checkout. It was when we came out that I realised that our little lectures on sharing were starting to have some effect; still with the highchair tucked under her arm, she emptied the remaining 70 pence out of her purse into a busker's hat, because 'I don't need anything else now and he might be hungry'. Talk to your children about the realities of life, tailoring it for each age group and trying not to frighten them as they imagine life on the streets, and you will be surprised at how much sense they have.

How much sense the adults have is another matter entirely. What might have seemed reasonable pre-baby can become shockingly frivolous or downright wasteful in the light of your new image as parents. Taking it down to basics, there are certain must-haves, as in a place to live, money to pay bills and food. However, that is about as basic as you can get, and most of us want a fair bit more. If you are living on benefits you will quite simply have no room to manoeuvre, and you don't need someone like me giving you patronising advice on how to manage the little cash you have, so I will keep it short. Make sure in the first instance that you are receiving everything you are entitled to, and double-check all rebates, such as housing benefit and council tax rebates. If you are living in local authority or housing association accommodation and you feel the standards are below par for your needs, then have this checked out. If you find dealing with figures in authority intimidating, go to your local councillor and ask them to check everything out for you. Most of them advertise their surgery dates and times in the local press, and are familiar with dealing with enquiries involving benefit or rent.

Handy Hints

If at all possible, pay for everything weekly so you are never in a situation where a big bill would completely floor you, and find out if there are any local support groups where you can get practical help. Some of these groups organise life-savers such as community shops, where food and other goods are sold as near to cost price as possible. If you are thinking about your prospects for the future, check local colleges for courses which would help your job chances, and remember that you might get the occasional privilege as a direct result of being unemployed, such as a nursery place for your child to enable you to take up a course of study. Whatever you do, if you get into debt do not go near money-lenders, tempting though the prospect of ready cash might be. Instead, go straight to your local Citizens Advice Bureau and ask them for help. They cannot supply cash assistance, but what they can and will do is contact any creditors you have and make arrangements to enable you to pay back your debt. The majority of creditors will be realistic enough to agree that having you pay back the debt at any rate is preferable to taking you to court, and with an organisation such as CAB assessing your income and ability to pay, a reasonable amount will be arranged. A hundred-pound debt might seem insurmountable if you have no extra income coming in, but if it is paid back at one or two pounds a week it becomes manageable.

This is a horrible situation to be in, especially if you cannot imagine a time when you will be able to get a job or the training to make a different life possible. It is not helped by the implication that you are a scrounger, and that the benefit you receive enables you to live a life of luxury. It would be interesting to see the main critics of families and single parents on benefit last as much as a week on the basic pittance they are expected to manage on. Try your best to think of your situation as temporary and consider what you would like to do in the future. You might have a better chance in some work areas if you have done even a little voluntary work which is related to your preferred field, so do some research and swap some baby-sitting with a friend to get the free time. If you start to mix with others it is surprising how profitable a bit of networking can be when it comes to future prospects.

If you are in the situation where only one of you is now working whereas previously you had two wages coming in and you are finding it difficult to manage, check first of all to see if you are entitled to family credit or any rent or council tax rebates. I recently interviewed a woman who was in this situation, and she said that her family was a typical example of the new poor in Britain. She and her husband had both worked when they first got married, and most of their money went on buying a two-bedroomed flat as an investment for the future. Like so many other young couples, they were actively encouraged to aim for home-ownership and this they duly did. Six years later they had the first of their three children, and after they decided that they couldn't afford to do without a second wage for a long period of time, the other two children followed in the next three years. Financially, life is a constant struggle, and although the wife is now working part time all her wages go on childcare.

She feels really bitter about their situation, despite the fact that their family life could not be warmer or more loving, because they are almost holding their breath for the children to reach school age which will enable her to earn some real money. They recently applied for benefit to top up the family income, only to discover that her husband's salary comes to £2 more a week than would qualify them for some help. Her summing-up is that there is an entire generation of families in this country who are one month's pay away from being bankrupt, and it is something you become aware of once you become parents.

If you have always managed to earn enough for a reasonable standard of living, having limitations suddenly put on spending can take some time to get used to. It is always a bit easier for a couple if they have had a few years together before settling into the restrictions caused by having a family, if only because you have experienced the nights out, holidays and spending which can be such a fun part of the transition from teenager to responsible adult. Somehow, it makes it easier to put all these luxuries on hold for a while if you can plan on going back to them at some time in the future.

Life is maybe not quite so simple if you are still very young or if you have not been together for very long, but there is no point in either of you trying to ignore your new circumstances or building up huge resentments. Work out your budget and, as I suggested before, pay as many bills as possible on a monthly basis. Mortgage, council tax, insurance policies and endowments are usually paid monthly anyway, but practically everything else can be adapted to suit, including gas, electricity and phone bills and TV licence. One smart move is to have payment dates adjusted so absolutely everything comes out of your bank account in the two or three days after pay-day, leaving you with the exact amount you then have to play with for the rest of the month.

Buying in bulk is not easy if you do not have much money to start with, but doing one massive monthly shop topped up by three small ones can really help save money. For me, food shopping is on a par with watching paint dry, but I have one enterprising friend who works out her menus a month in advance and shops accordingly. She also cooks in bulk and makes the best use of her freezer, buys all her fruit from the market rather than the supermarket, and buys up bread and rolls on their sell-by date and freezes them. You need to be organised to do this, but she says that the effort involved for a week out of every month saves her a lot in cash terms, while also making her feel that she is making the most of their limited finances. This is now a way of life with her, to the extent that at any given time she has a vague idea of how many birthdays are coming up and makes sure that presents are bought in advance, usually in the sales. Mind you, it must also be said that anyone less like Scrooge would be difficult to imagine, as any money saved is carefully hoarded to improve the quality of life, with something like a nice bottle of wine, a night at the pictures or pantomime tickets for the family. I have to admit that although I try to follow her example I am not nearly so organised, although there are certain things like nappies which I always buy in bulk. However, she is a perfect example of how to make every penny count without turning into a kill-joy, and she also maintains that this careful way of life is only until she is back to work, when she intends to take up riotous living with a vengeance!

GOOD LAWYERS

An ideal investment is a good lawyer, who is ready to advise you on the big things, such as your mortgage. If you are in the position of having to move house, you need someone with business sense to look at your options. Assuming that your income is likely to be fixed and insufficient for the next few years, it might be a good time to consider a fixed-rate mortgage to go with it, so you do not reel in shock every time there is the slightest possibility of a rise in interest rates. Even if you plan to stay where you are you should reconsider your mortgage options from time to time to make sure that you are getting the best deal. Various banks and building societies now claim to have mortgages tailor-made for people with young families, but it is best to contact them direct to see what they have to offer at any one time. Reduced and deferred payments can sound very attractive, but get your trusty lawyer to work it out in hard cash before you sign on the dotted line. You don't get anything for nothing, but you might fancy the idea of paying a bit more in the future if you can pay a bit less now.

There is a lot of competition, so now is the time to take up hard bargaining as a hobby. Always stay friends with your bank or building society and feel free to go to them and say, 'I have been a valued customer for x number of years and I assume you want to keep me. The Bank of Blah down the road has offered me this rate for the next three years. Can you match this?' You will be surprised at just how much they do want to keep you, and the same applies to insurance companies dealing with car, home and buildings. If you do not ask you have got no chance of getting, and if you are in a union at work check to see if they have a special arrangement with any insurance company which gives their members special rates.

On the subject of cars, if yours is provided by your company then make the most of it, as it is an excellent perk. In all other cases, is a car a luxury or a necessity? It certainly makes life a lot easier when it comes to the drudgery of shopping or the fun of days out, but unless you are a dab hand at DIY car maintenance it costs a lot of money to maintain. Again, if you decide that it is something you cannot live without, then shop around for the best bargain. An old cheap number might appeal, but it is a false economy if it breaks down constantly or costs a lot in repair bills. Keep a look out for special offers on new cars, the best being the 0 % finance which crops up from time to time, and when it comes to insurance go back to shopping around for the best deal.

The most tempting yet irritating thing to happen to you at this time is that you will be inundated with letters offering all sorts of credit cards and loans from some very reputable companies who should know a lot better. Sticking to a tight budget can be achieved, but you never know when something is going to knock you off your even keel, be it a leaking roof or a broken-down washing machine. It is always handy to know that you can use your credit card to bail you out, but it must be viewed as an emergency solution, to be paid back as soon as possible. Sometimes credit cards can quite rightly fund straightforward fun, such as a family wedding or a weekend away, but these are one-off situations which you will then have to include in your budget calculations over the next six months as you pay off the bills.

There are part-time jobs which are particularly seasonal, as I mentioned before, and can see you over Christmas or birthdays. Having child benefit paid into a separate account and trying to save it for special events is something that some people manage very well, simply by pretending that it isn't there. Using it to buy shoes or winter jackets or to subsidise Christmas without dipping into the normal budget can make a great difference to your household accounts, although I think you need to be very determined not to use it when there is a week to pay-day and you don't have a brass farthing.

Keep on Top of your Finances

If your accounts are starting to take on a nasty reddish hue, then contact the bank long before they write to you, as they will charge a hefty £15 to £20 for doing so, as well as slapping on penalty interest payments for unauthorised overdrafts. I know you can sometimes get the impression that bank staff are less than human, but it helps if they know you, you keep them informed about your financial affairs and you stay realistic about managing your money. Having said that, if you do have an agreed overdraft they are certainly not giving you money for nothing, so grovelling humility is not necessary. Banks lend money to make money, won't do so if you are not a good risk and like to keep their customers, so don't be messed around. Always check bank statements for interest charges or any of those nasty hidden extras, but always be one step ahead of them.

This is particularly true if you are self-employed and trying to reconcile cash flow, as bank managers can be quite understanding about this problem and therefore willing to set an overdraft allowance for even just a few days to tide you over, sometimes without penalty. The bottom line is that you should stick with your bank if you feel they give reasonable service, and understand that the majority of couples will have a few lean years if they have young children. However, any bank managers worth their salt should realise that treating you well while you are poor should ensure that you are a customer for life once you become affluent again; if they are not long-sighted enough to realise this, do they have the business sense you would like in someone handling your finances?

It can be a real pain always having to look for bargains, but there is not a lot of sense in wasting money you do not have. Any circle of parents will have a jungle drums system which passes on all the information about sales, special bargains or factory shops, and once there is a crowd of friends with children you automatically start passing clothes around. Even expensive buys like shoes can be less so if you use good quality factory or clearance shops, and wellies, slippers and sandshoes can be bought a lot cheaper than the brand-name products. Although well-fitted shoes are an absolute must, other types of footwear are on for such short bursts of time that there isn't the same necessity for them to be absolutely perfect. Martyrdom is not an integral part of parenthood, but considering that children grow like sunflowers and you don't, somehow it becomes easier to forego a new winter jacket for the third year in a row and spend the money on something cosy for your toddler instead. This becomes so automatic that you don't even consider resenting it, and then one day you have enough cash to spend some on yourself and it comes as a total shock to realise how long it is since you have had something new to wear.

Toys are necessities, not luxuries, according to children, but it is hard not to be able to buy them everything they want. Use toy shops like The Early Learning Centre for good quality, fun things which stimulate your children's imagination, and join the library with them at a really early age. Teach them to respect books and they will get untold enjoyment out of the whole outing; picking books, reading them at home with you and carefully returning them. Even children as young as one thrive on the mixture of responsibility and fun involved, and in some areas you will even find Toy Libraries, which are exactly as they sound. It is a super way for children to try out different toys, and gives you a clear indication of what will be well played with before you buy for birthdays and Christmas. Some toys are made to last, and can be picked up for a song second hand. The obvious ones are bikes and trikes, but just make sure that brakes and tyres are up to standard. Play equipment such as swings, slides and heavy-duty plastic playhouses seem to go on for ever and are virtually unbreakable, so check out the 'snips' in your local paper for the best bargains.

Toys that you do buy first hand should be safe, without any dangerous little pieces which could come loose and constitute a choking hazard. Always keep receipts in case of problems, and never be fobbed off by shopkeepers suggesting that you are responsible for sending faulty goods back to the manufacturer. The contract of sale is between you and the shop, so stand your ground and be pleasant but immovable. If you are getting nowhere, make sure you return at one of their busiest times and speak in clear, carrying tones which allow every potential customer to hear about your problem. You should find that the staff will then fall over themselves to sort everything out for you.

PLAN FOR THE FUTURE

A worthwhile investment for the future is making sure you pay your national insurance contributions, especially if you are self-employed. You can really benefit when it comes to another pregnancy, making you eligible for 18 weeks of maternity allowance, and possibly sickness benefit thereafter if you are unfit to work. Furthermore, far away though it sounds, these contributions will be counted in assessing your pension. If you are self-employed and doing your own tax returns, make sure that you claim for all relevant expenses over and above your personal allowance. Keep meticulous records and all receipts, even if you then pass the whole lot to an accountant to put in order. If your business is small or relatively straightforward, you should be able to keep the books yourself. The Inland Revenue have recently started self-assessment for anyone self-employed who is earning less than £15,000 a year, and the accompanying forms are surprisingly straightforward. If in doubt, ask either an adviser at your local development agency or phone up the Inland Revenue and find out who deals with you. Once you actually have a name to refer to and discover that they are not all ogres, they can make life very simple.

When it comes to benefit claims every department has a bad name in relation to customer care, possibly due to them being overworked and understaffed, apart from one. The Contributions Agency based in Newcastle, which handles self-employment details such as payment of national insurance, seems to be staffed entirely by the most courteous, well-informed civil servants imaginable who more than deserve that adjective. They will happily explain pension forecasts, personal allowances and the different classes of contribution to anyone who cares to ask, and will answer the most inane questions without losing patience.

As your children get older you will be faced with some expenses you just cannot ignore, such as school uniform. Blazers are particularly impractical garments – too hot in summer and not warm enough in winter – but don't the little darlings look smart in them? They are an excellent item for passing on, and if you do not already know someone at the school who could provide you with one, you will probably find that there is a good second-hand scheme run by the PTA. I don't know how we manage it, but most of us cough up for an entirely new ensemble for the first child, but, as with everything else, our standards drop dramatically with every subsequent sibling. When I discovered that the regulation colours hat, scarf and gloves would set me back by nearly thirty pounds, I went back to the ancient art of knitting, and after a frenzied weekend managed to produce the required garments for a grand total of £2.86. On Granny's advice I then attached scarf and gloves at appropriate points to the school coat, which saved me permanently rooting through the lost-property box in the cloakroom. Packed lunches and play pieces can add a considerable amount to the weekly food bill, if your children show a liking for those nifty little cartons of juice and bags of crisps. Compromise, buy the miniature juice cartons in bulk and issue them for interval time only, and get a leak-proof flask for diluted juice in the lunch box.

Money concerns are a fact of life but they shouldn't be all-consuming unless a major problem crops up, such as redundancy or your house collapsing around your ears, in which case you need the experts to point you in the right direction. For the rest of us, if you are living on a tight budget then get it as organised as possible without turning life into a miserable economy drive. We all know people who go on and on about lack of money until you could scream; they are usually the ones who turn up at the pub and 'forget' to bring any cash so in the end they probably have a lot more than the poor suckers they mix with! If you can't afford to get involved in some activity then just say so, but without putting friends and family under any pressure to subsidise you. Similarly, if your children want to go horse riding and dancing and there is no way you can afford both, then tell them and help them decide which they would prefer.

It is not the end of the world if you have to watch your cash for a few years, although it could certainly seem like it if you got yourselves into horrendous debt because you couldn't bear having to juggle your finances. If you feel really hard done by because foreign holidays or some other treat from the past has disappeared, then consider whether it means so much to you that it is worth while doing something extra like pub work or party plan just to save up for it. Whatever situation you are in can be changed if that is what you really want, but what you are aiming for at the moment is a compromise which allows peace of mind, time with your children, time with your partner, job satisfaction – no matter if that is as stay-at-home mum or president of a huge company – and enough money to get by. Anything else is a bonus.

Chapter Nine

When Things Go Wrong

More than anything I wish for guarantees, both for me and for you. If only someone would come up with some scheme, or form of treatment, that would ensure perfect pregnancies ending in ideal births, and gift the children long life and health. It is, however, as unrealistic as wishing for the moon. Even before you become pregnant you find yourself making bargains with God, or whoever you believe in. 'Please let me be pregnant this month, and let everything be all right,' you say, ignoring the obvious period cramps and the PMT which you make sure your partner suffers from instead of yourself. When you do conceive you cannot help but worry, and every little twinge and unusual symptom has you leafing through your trusty reference book, but deep down you are convinced that everything will be fine, and that is the only way to approach your pregnancy – otherwise, you would be a gibbering wreck from start to finish. Even when you read about all the different things that could go wrong it is out of natural curiosity, because nothing like that could ever happen to you. Consequently, if anything happens which is not in your plan, you are totally unprepared for the shock. A 'normal' pregnancy is enough of a new experience, and the general information you receive is so focused on standard treatment and results that if anything out of the ordinary happens, you tend to feel very isolated and very frightened.

DECIDING ABOUT TESTING

As I explained in chapter one, most couples reach a point where they cannot help but wonder if everything is developing as it should, and make a decision about which tests they will opt for. All the non-invasive tests provide an answer based around chance, which must be taken in perspective. For example, if there is a 1 in 250 chance that women of a certain age group will have a baby with a certain condition, although all of them will have the same chance of this happening, in reality 249 of them will deliver a normal child. It is a hard concept to grasp, especially if you have never considered the possibilities of testing, nor what your reaction would be if you had a worrying result.

For some couples the decision is already made before they undergo any tests, the couple knowing that they would never have a termination. It might seem strange to go through testing if that is your first and last decision, but if the couple would prefer to prepare themselves for any problems, that is an entirely personal choice. Sadly, there are an awful lot of people over-ready with an opinion about an already traumatic experience, and I would suggest keeping your considerations to yourselves until, or even after, you know what you plan to do. The few women I know who have gone through a termination found it an intensely emotional and distressing experience, and none of them had the 'contraception option' attitude which periodically makes headlines in the gutter press.

If you feel that you would like to opt for standard tests before making any further decisions, remember that one thing may lead to another very quickly from the moment a worrying result is discovered. I mean this not in relation to your hospital, but instead regarding your own emotions. You will need to accept that taking one test may produce a result which makes you want to know more, so in a very short space of time you could find yourself considering testing which had never occurred to you previously. The miscarriage risk which automatically comes with invasive testing such as amniocentesis and chorionic villus sampling far outweighs their definitive results as far as some people are concerned. Unfortunately this is a decision which you must make yourselves, and although the staff will undoubtedly be supportive and caring, their job is to make sure that you know everything possible to enable you to make such a choice.

You simply cannot quantify the grief suffered as a result of miscarrying after invasive testing, irrespective of whether or not the child was healthy. All you and your emotions know is that you were pregnant, and now you are not. You can never know if you would have miscarried anyway, but blaming yourself is the obvious reaction. This is bound to have a lasting effect on any subsequent pregnancies, and you need to talk to the experts in your hospital who deal with pre-conception care. There is a theory that the staff who do specialise in this area will be blasé or uncaring about a worrying result or miscarriage because they deal with this on a day-to-day basis. I cannot emphasise enough how much the opposite is true; you will find them a constant help and strength for as long as you need them, whether it is months or years. They see many happy outcomes, but the very nature of their job means that they also see a lot of pain. Each patient will be treated as their own circumstances demand, and not as just another statistic.

When you reach a time where your worst fears are confirmed and you are advised that the condition you feared is present, any previous decisions seem to have been taken in the dim and distant past. A common reaction is to ask if there is any possibility of a mistake being made in the testing, and in some cases an earlier choice no longer appears as straightforward as was first thought. I am assuming that you are in a situation where your pregnancy is wanted and it is not in the very early stages, otherwise it is unlikely that you would be reading a book like this.

If you are uncertain, perhaps because you are starting to feel that you will cope no matter what your child suffers from, or because you know very little about their condition and its implications, then tell the medical staff and ask for their help. Don't get the idea that they are in the business of producing only perfect human beings, when in fact they are there to help you reach the right choice for you. If you want to find out more about a heart condition, spina bifida or Down's syndrome, they will have contact numbers to get you talking to the right people. These will be people who have been there before you and know exactly what you are going through.

TERMINATION

Deciding that a termination is for you is also something that is your business and yours alone. If you want to share it with your mum or close friends then go ahead, but this is not the time to feel under pressure to make a stand on behalf of the sisterhood and shout for a right to choose. One woman I spoke to told me that she felt so guilty about her decision that she told everyone, just waiting to be punished verbally for doing such a shocking thing, but it didn't work like that. Most people are too aware of the 'there but for the grace of God' concept to hurt someone in such obvious pain, although there is always the chance of some unsympathetic so-called Christian putting the boot in. Tell the world that you have miscarried if that is what you would prefer, and take all the nurturing and care that you are due because, however you put it, you have suffered a terrible bereavement.

An early termination, up to 14 weeks, will probably be done under a general anaesthetic, although for a later termination you will probably have to go through labour. At this stage you may want to see or hold your baby or come up with a name, but if you cannot face this you could ask the hospital staff to take a photo, which you may find it comforting to have at a later date. Don't expect to bounce back quickly, and if counselling would help then go for it. If you are planning to conceive again, keep in touch with the pre-conception care unit at your hospital, and take their advice. Be gentle with each other, and with yourselves.

CONTINUING THE PREGNANCY

Deciding to go ahead with your pregnancy takes another kind of courage, but you too will be experiencing a bereavement. It is the end of your original hopes for a 'perfect' child, and you cannot help but grieve for that. Your grief is not just for the baby and what it will have to face in life, but what you will go through as loving parents. It might make it slightly easier if you can tell people what has happened, even if it is just those closest to you. As well as coming to terms with your own feelings, you will have to be prepared for the sort of crass remark that the most sensitive person can come out with, simply because they desperately want to be helpful and don't have a clue what to say. Stay in touch with any organisations you have contacted for support, and remember that you do not have to be a pillar of strength all the time – if you want to scream with rage then turn to your closest friends, and if you don't feel that you can inflict that on them, phone The Samaritans.

When your baby is born, depending on her condition, you will get some support from social services, but the general impression I have been given about this is that you have to ask fairly persistently to make sure you do get the help you need. The same applies to those who had not opted for testing and who are therefore shocked to discover at the birth that their baby has a disability of some kind. Disability is a very general term which can cover everything from a condition like Down's syndrome to a child born very prematurely, with all the problems which that can bring. In the past there were depressing stories of medical staff being unable to deal tactfully with telling parents that their child had a problem, but fortunately this is a lot less common nowadays, as emphasis is placed on good counselling skills. After the initial shock has passed, these are the people who will be there for you in the middle of the night and who will keep you going through the first week as you try to come to terms with what has happened, and they will provide a crutch you will probably never forget.

Premature Births

Situations such as very premature birth can leave parents feeling like total failures, because so much of their baby's care has to be left to the experts, but more and more special care baby units are investigating and introducing ways of involving parents in a much more positive way. One particularly successful venture has been the introduction of Kangaroo Care, where the tiniest babies are nursed against the parents' skin while still wired up to the latest technology. Many mothers of premature babies will express milk so successfully that by the time the baby is off the machinery and able to suck, their milk production will be in full flow. Kangaroo Care is something that fathers can also get involved in. Seeing your baby in the midst of life-saving equipment is at the same time terrifying and reassuring, but most hospitals encourage parents practically to live-in with their child and get involved in their care. As time goes by the machinery becomes less imposing and you are able to accept it for the life-saver it is, but this is a very tense situation to live through, especially as some babies will be kept in hospital for months rather than weeks. All babies who needed special or intensive care will be monitored for a considerable time after leaving hospital, with developmental checks becoming a regular thing probably until the child reaches school age.

THE LOSS OF A CHILD

The worst thing that can ever happen is the death of a child, and the feelings of guilt and injustice can be overwhelming. The pain of one loss should never be measured against another, although logically you cannot help but feel that there has to be some difference between an early miscarriage and a stillbirth. For the people in the middle of the experience, quantifying their pain in the light of someone else's tragedy serves no useful purpose, so each situation should be treated as carefully as possible.

An ectopic pregnancy occurs when a fertilised egg does not move into the womb but instead implants itself in one of the fallopian tubes. You may think that everything is straightforward, especially if you have had a positive pregnancy test. However, shortly after a missed period you are likely to experience some warning signs, such as a severe pain low down in the abdomen on one side, vaginal bleeding and sometimes a feeling of faintness. The ectopic pregnancy is usually detected by ultrasound scanning, whereupon it must be removed to prevent rupturing. Traditionally this treatment involved removing the fallopian tube, which naturally decreased fertility, but doctors will now attempt to preserve the tube if at all possible. You do not have a choice when it comes to ectopic pregnancy, because of the very high chance of maternal mortality along with the certainty of foetal death. It is also a condition which does have a tendency to recur, which is infinitely depressing if you are desperate to conceive. However, very early scanning will be offered during any subsequent pregnancies, either giving you peace of mind or ensuring that the least damage possible is done to your fallopian tube during removal of the foetus.

Miscarriage is one of those words that is surrounded by statistics, as in 'it is estimated that as many as one in four pregnancies end in a miscarriage', which is of neither help nor comfort when it happens to you. An early miscarriage is rather like a period, whereas one that happens between three and six months is more like a labour. Realising that you are bleeding at any stage of pregnancy is terrifying, but in some cases it will simply stop and everything will go on as normal. Some doctors are very fond of saying that if a pregnancy is going to last then practically nothing can jeopardise it, while one that is unstable for any reason is going to end anyway. This may be true, but the moment you become pregnant you cannot help but start to feel responsible for your baby, and these feelings are very difficult to reconcile with attitudes such as 'there must be something wrong with it' or 'it's nature's way of sorting out problems'.

Whatever happens you are going to feel responsible for it, no matter what the medical experts say, but the world is full of tactless people making comments about it being too early to matter or how you can always have another one. Maybe so, but not this one, and right now this is who you want to be growing perfectly inside you. One of the hardest ways to find out that you have lost your baby is by going for a scan, and despite having no symptoms at all, being told that the baby has died. This is another of these heart-rending situations where you try to convince yourself that a mistake has been made and the next scan will prove it. Tell the staff, and they will arrange another scan to reassure you, especially if you have to undergo a D and C to empty the womb. Usually they will attempt some form of laboratory analysis to ascertain whether there was a genetic or attributable cause for the miscarriage. It is, however, unlikely that they will be able to give you a definitive answer, which can be hard to bear.

Will you try again after going through an ectopic pregnancy or miscarriage? No one can make that decision for you, and, sadly, no one can give you any guarantees for the future. If you do decide to try again, be guided by your doctor on how long you should wait and, depressing though this is, you will probably have to accept that any subsequent pregnancies are going to be fraught with worry. Don't put yourself under any extra pressure to keep a stiff upper lip when in reality you are utterly petrified, spending half the day dashing to the toilet to check that you haven't started bleeding and lying awake night after night imagining what can go wrong. Talking about your worries to your partner, close friend or doctor will help a bit, but you simply cannot be as carefree about being pregnant ever again. Sometimes just accepting that you will be unable to relax until the baby arrives safely is enough to calm you down, but it is not going to be an easy nine months, no matter how you approach it.

The most difficult article I have ever had to research and write concerned child death, and although I managed not to cry in front of the bereaved parents whom I interviewed, I simply could not stop weeping as I actually wrote the piece. Part of this empathy has to be fear, imagining the horror of being in their situation, and part of it is bound up in the traditions of this country, where we don't make emotion public. All the people I spoke to, whether they lost a child in pregnancy, in a stillbirth or even later, claimed that their anguish was made worse by the embarrassment they caused other people, who simply did not know how to help. No one can help, but for relatives struggling to come to terms with what has happened, an acknowledgement that their child did exist is a start. One young father told me that after initial sympathy from his colleagues over his baby daughter's death, within a couple of weeks she was never mentioned. Yet while he would be crying at her grave which was so obviously a child's, complete strangers would come and wrap their arms around him and weep with him. One elderly lady rocked him like a baby, saying 'just cry, son' over and over again, then mopped up his tears and kissed him goodbye. Meanwhile, his best friend and partner at work would briskly suggest a quick pint, and sympathy took the form of a pat on the shoulder. Sometimes he felt his daughter had never existed.

There is so much officialdom attached to death that the bereaved can feel swept away by activity, but even if you have to undergo the pain of knowing that there has to be a post-mortem, medical staff will be on hand to make sure you get to have a quiet time with your baby to say goodbye. Ask for your minister or priest and have your baby baptised, if this is what you want, or take photographs for a memento. Some hospitals have a Book of Remembrance kept in their chapel, where a record of your baby's birth and death will be kept. If you want to talk to a counsellor at some point then ask the hospital to give you details of who to contact, but if you feel better able to deal with your feelings privately then trust your instincts. I hope you never have to read this chapter from the personal perspective of experiencing anything similar, but if you know anyone who has, then let them know you are thinking about them. You cope with tragedies like this only because you cannot do anything else, and I wish I could tell you that it gets better, but those who have gone through it tell me that you only learn to live with it.

Chapter Ten

Doing It All Again

It is difficult to imagine loving anyone as much as your first-born, and for a while after their arrival it never even crosses your mind. You might have moments when you wonder why your child is so much better looking, talented and downright cute than any other child you have ever met, but eventually you just accept that as a fact of life. You have days where you are more than coping and life is a joy, and then you have the sort of days which make you wonder why you ever thought you were a half-decent parent. This is not only normal, but it is nature's way of breaking you in gently to the next stage. Your baby may be the cuddliest, cutest little coochy-coo in creation, but don't forget that all children have got their very own little character. Even as they beam at you gummily and you melt in adoration, they are hurtling towards a time in their lives which, I have been assured, lasts for approximately 18 years: the assertive phase.

'The Terrible Twos' is a favoured phrase, and to my mind a total misnomer. Are we planning to ignore the Overactive Ones, the Terrorising Threes and the Furious Fours? While we are at it, don't the Firm Fives deserve a mention? All children have particular character traits which mark them out as individuals, and although we might try and guide them, we have no chance of making any radical changes. It is especially irritating when they start to develop an obnoxious mixture of the worst sides of you and your partner, and you find yourself locked in battle with your mirror image. It is surprising how often this realisation coincides with a discussion about the possibility of having another baby, and you drop the subject like the proverbial hot potato. Some of you may find yourselves going through this in duplicate, having had two children within a short time-scale like a year, or you may wonder why one is so assertive and the other so relaxed. Don't torture yourself, because it is like the Mona Lisa's smile – no one knows.

Having gone through the stunning experience of parenthood, what on earth makes people contemplate it for a second time? The answer to that has the same logic as the reasons why you did it the first time, which is anything at all which seems like a good excuse at the time. Besides, once you have had your own baby they become very addictive, although that is probably not the best reason for having a family of ten. If you have already decided that one is more than enough, thank you, then ignore this chapter, because it is unlikely to change your mind.

AGE GAPS

For those who have decided to go for it, is there such a thing as the ideal age gap? Sometimes, straight logic comes into it, where you decide that you would like four children very close together so that the total disruption is over in one go, and they will be company for each other. Mind you, there are some who would say that that is not logic, but the workings of a clearly deranged mind! On the most practical note, consider money, careers, health and housing and then make your decision. A more usual scenario is for both of you to feel at the same time that a new baby is a good idea, so hang the finances.

All age gaps have their own advantages and disadvantages, from both the parents' and children's points of view. If the children are very close together they certainly won't have had time to establish territorial rights and will never remember a time without their brother or sister, but you might feel that you are living in an endless rut of 'babydom' and there is a limit to how many sleepless nights you can put up with. If there are two to three years between children it takes a lot of work to make sure that the older child does not feel usurped, especially as babies have the cuteness appeal which is not quite so noticeable in a runny-nosed two-year-old having a tantrum. However, this sort of gap does give you the chance to get back into some sort of shape (pause for a hollow laugh) and to establish a routine of some kind. Your first child might even be out of nappies and able to walk further than three feet without dashing into the road.

A bigger gap, of five years or more, is less common, and is far enough away from the reality of the first few months to make it like starting all over again, complete with all the startling implications involved in that idea. However, the chances are that school-age children will be able to face the changes with far more equanimity than their parents and, if they are in the mood, will be at an excellent age to offer some real help.

A NEW KIND OF GUILT

Deciding to have another baby is another excuse to indulge in some useless guilt, but since this has now become an intrinsic part of life you will suffer in anything but silence, winding each other up to the skies about how your first-born will be angst-ridden by this shocking change to their life. If you have been the centre of two people's attention for a few years and then someone else comes along to share your throne, of course it takes a bit of getting used to, but it is not the end of the world. However, if you handle the whole event as either a tragedy or the most exciting thing since man walked on the moon, then you are asking for trouble.

My main concern with my second pregnancy was not so much guilt about my first daughter's reaction, because I was convinced that she would eventually enjoy having a brother or sister, but worry that I would be letting the second baby down by not loving her. More rational people have a lot more sense than that, just assuming that nature will take over and they will love the second as much as the first, but it is a very real fear for a great many second-time parents. You will find a change of emphasis in a second pregnancy, as you don't spend the same amount of time working out development stages or simply musing about baby bootees, although that really comes back to being too busy.

Absolutely the worst thing about a second or subsequent pregnancy has to be experiencing things like sickness while older children are bouncing around the place. Even if you are daft enough to tell them about the new baby that early – you then have to endure months of 'when will it be here?' until you are fit to scream – they have no idea how awful you are feeling, and why should they? My only recommendation for this situation is to make sure that your partner is quite prepared to do as much as possible chore-wise, and to get a Chrissy.

Unfortunately, this is a particularly rare kind of friend, and if you don't have one already then there is not a lot you can do. Not only does she have an unerring instinct for knowing the exact moment when life is getting on top of you, she puts this into action by whipping your children away for a few hours to play with hers and allowing you to get some much-needed sleep, or just letting you shove your head down the loo in peace. Now logically you know that this must result in moments of pure bedlam for her, but she also has the perfect knack of airily dismissing your qualms and making you feel that it was no bother at all. There is no down-side to this arrangement, unless you count the fact that your children worship the ground she walks on, prefer her to you any day of the week, and plan to move in with her every time they fall out with you. I cannot fault the argument, because sometimes I could just come with them! However, all joking apart, this is the sort of support which makes surviving not just possible, but at times even enjoyable, especially when you start to get excited about the forthcoming event.

Once you get into the swing of it, this pregnancy becomes as important as the first, especially since you now know what you will get at the end of it. You imagine that you will get a carbon copy of No. 1, despite knowing that this is fairly unlikely. Perhaps you will be desperate for the opposite gender to that of the baby you have now, but the chances of choosing the baby's sex have not improved since the first time round.

Antenatal classes are like a refresher course, although now you know why the waiting-rooms are creaking with toys as you try to persuade your two-year-old to calm down. The consultants and midwives welcome you back like an old friend and are completely relaxed about your toddler demanding to climb on the bed with you, or scowling at all the nurses who are trying to entertain your little horror. You know they are thinking, 'Why on earth is she going for another one when her first is such a nightmare?' but these people are beautifully trained and reassure you that life will be a ball. For me, going for my scan was the moment which confirmed that we had been right to have another. Older, wiser and more cynical though we were, seeing the tiny figure on the screen was as moving as the first time, and despite my two-year-old loudly telling the doctor, 'Don't put jelly on Mummy's tummy – you're meant to eat it!', none of the magic was lost. We had given her crisps to distract her, and her happy munching just added to the moment – which goes a long way towards illustrating what doting idiots we are.

REASSURING OLDER CHILDREN

When you get around to telling older children about the new baby, be as matter of fact as possible. One of the nicest approaches I have heard of is to tell them that they have been such a success that you fancied trying to repeat it. Have the decency to listen to any worries they might have and acknowledge them. It is dismissive in the extreme if every concern is met with a bland 'don't worry, everything will be fine' when these worries are overwhelming to small children. If they are very young they won't really register any difference until the baby has actually arrived, but most two-year-olds can get themselves very bogged down in worries that they are going to be replaced, that they have been so naughty that the baby is a punishment, or even that they will lose the old familiar things like their cot to this new arrival. Don't suddenly start potty training to make sure that you won't be changing two lots of nappies, as this event should not be hurried for anyone. When they are good and ready they will take to it with enthusiasm, but should receive gentle encouragement rather than any form of ticking-off for little accidents. If you do hustle them out of nappies too quickly, you can bet your bottom dollar that they will regress the moment the sibling arrives, and that can be extremely traumatic for all parties concerned.

Children are all intensely curious but at differing paces, so once you have told them that you are growing a baby, don't go on and on about it. It takes a long time to materialise in their little worlds, so an occasional reference will be more than enough to keep the idea fresh. There are some lovely books which you can read together, dealing very sensitively with all the complex emotions that can arise within a family, and allowing children to think through their worries.

Later on, as you start to resemble a whale and say things like 'don't stand on my tummy!', they are confronted by some very obvious evidence that life will never be the same again, and you become an object of curiosity, as little fingers poke at your tummy and little heads try to listen to the baby. Let them treat you like Exhibit A, because at the moment you have the extra appeal that you usually only get with other people's pets and wriggly worms. Get them involved in discussions about names, and if you are having a hospital birth, tell them exactly what will be happening to them. If they are going to be staying with Granny, or if she is moving in for a few days, make it seem like an adventure. If they point out rather petulantly that they will miss you, then reassure them that you will be missing them even more and be desperate to get home to them. I was advised to try straightforward bribery and corruption to minimise trauma, and I have to say it worked beautifully.

SPOIL THEM

Fill your hospital bag with a selection of brightly wrapped little presents, to be doled out at the end of visiting time and opened on the way home. No matter how much you are missing them, remember that hospitals are both boring and intimidating for small children, so one visit a day for a couple of hours is probably their maximum. If you find it hard going, remember that you are big enough and ugly enough to look after yourself. Encourage shameless spoiling while you are in hospital, and try to get back to normal routine as soon as you get home.

The first time they come to see you after the birth, try and concentrate on them and pay little attention to the new baby, apart from making sure that there is something yummy in the cot, like a packet of chocolate buttons. These children have years to get acquainted, so don't put them off by over-enthusiastic cooing or forcing them to acknowledge that the baby is lovely. It's just a baby, it's keeping Mummy in hospital and it doesn't do anything exciting. Give them all a chance and remember that you can't win. When my second daughter was born she was a great sleeper, so I was delighted at how little our routine was disrupted, until the eldest said with total disgust: 'She's really boring – all she does is eat and sleep.' Like I said, you can't win.

If you have had a section or stitches you will have to be brave about it in case you frighten your children, who don't like illness in their parents, so try not to be lying on the bed doing your dying swan act when they arrive. Escorting them to the door when they go seems to be a trigger for copious tears, so a kiss and a hug in the ward should be attempted, especially if the presents succeeded in distracting them. Resist the temptation to phone home for little chats, as this can be another reminder that you are not there, so wait until you are sure they are in bed before telling your partner about all the endearing little habits of your new baby. If your partner has time off with the family while you are in hospital, he can transform a possibly upsetting experience into a holiday, and a bit of partying never hurt anyone. I know that in this house we are positively encouraged to have babies, because you have such a great time with Daddy while Mummy is stuck in hospital.

Expect a bit of a mess when you get home and don't imagine much of a routine for a while, but you will be surprised at how laid back you are this time. You won't have the same time to meander about getting ready, especially if there are other little ones to feed or get ready for school, but with any luck Granny will turn up again just when you need her most. Any visitors who have tactless tendencies should be firmly distracted, as immediate attention should not be given to the new baby as opposed to the old. Keep a store of treats for emergencies, although most people will be smart enough to anticipate jealousy and so fuss over the older ones.

Try and act as if the baby belongs to the older brother or sister, and grit your teeth when they get a bit careless in holding or cuddling. If you leap in anguish every time they touch the infant they have got very little chance of establishing any relationship beyond resentment, and you have to accept that their entire world is in turmoil for some time. Be prepared for sulks, tantrums and any other attention-seeking behaviour, but don't be manipulated. Let them know that you love the boots off them and that they have a very special place in the family, but that their little brother or sister does too.

Sometimes you think you have escaped unscathed for a year or so and you wonder why people are concerned about sibling rivalry, and then the younger one starts asserting themselves and the older goes bananas. No family is perfect, and if you have had convenient memory loss which means that you have forgotten any punch-up you ever had with your siblings, then the average scrap can leave you feeling that the world is falling apart. Things will settle down, but the best way to approach it is to try not only to be fair, but to be seen to be fair, which children set great store by.

Enjoy It All

From now on, all you do is live and learn. How many children you want, how you bring them up and what you hope for their future is your personal dream, but it is amazing how quickly it can also become your life's work. Having a baby is a million miles away from what you thought it would be like, but also a million times better. The trouble with sharing all the possible problems is that they can appear to be more important than the best bits, yet nothing could be further from the truth. Knowing how to deal with the hiccups makes the rest so much better, and there are some moments which are priceless: holding your tiny baby and simply admiring her little bare feet, watching your children sleep and wondering what dreams are making them smile, being able to kiss them better when no one else can, and crying during their nativity play. Some things only a parent can do, and it doesn't matter if your children are five or forty – no one can love them like you do.

Useful Contacts

Association of Breastfeeding Mothers
26 Holmshaw Close
London SE26 4TH
0181 778 4769

Association for Post-Natal Illness
25 Jerdan Place
London SW6 1BE
0171 386 0868

British Diabetic Association
Check telephone directory for local contact

Caesarean Support Network
Phone 01624 661269 for local contact

Citizens Advice Bureau
Check telephone directory for local contact

CRY-SIS
BM CRY-SIS
London WC1N 3XX
0171 404 5011

USEFUL CONTACTS

Disfigurement Guidance Centre
PO Box 7
Cupar
Fife KY15 4PF
01337 870281

Family Welfare Association
501–505 Kingsland Road
London E8 4AU
0171 254 6251

Gingerbread
Check telephone directory for local contact

La Leche League
BM 3424
London WC1N 3XX
0171 242 1278

MAMA (Meet a mum)
Phone 0181 665 0357 for local contact

National AIDS Helpline 0800 567 123

National Childbirth Trust
Alexandra House
Oldham Terrace
Acton
London W3 6NH
0181 992 8637

Smokeline 0800 84 84 84
Help and support for those trying to stop smoking